Please Miss

We stood face to face, the regulation stance for opponents in many trials of strength. Suddenly I realised the enormity of my handicap. I was outnumbered by forty to one. I had only one obvious advantage over the children. I was bigger than they were.

Whether school days are the happiest days of your life depends to some extent of course which side of the desk you are speaking from. This lively story of what a term in the teaching profession can involve suggests that, to take on such sparring partners as this set of tough-minded sturdily independent youngsters, you should have the staying power of an ox and an outsize sense of humour. If your subjects are English and Music, it can of course be a relief, albeit a humiliation to be confronted with a pint-size Euclid to tot up dinner money or sportsday scoring for you. And a pupil with a father to provide you – from his own scrapyard? – with an elderly but generally roadworthy car is not to be sniffed at . . . though can the same, one wonders, be said for Sweet William?

Please Miss

VICKY BRANDRICK

London
MICHAEL JOSEPH

First published in Great Britain by
MICHAEL JOSEPH LTD
26 Bloomsbury Street
London, W.C.1
1966

Set and printed in Great Britain by Tonbridge Printers Ltd, Peach Hall Works, Tonbridge, Kent, in Bembo twelve on fourteen point, on paper made by Henry Bruce at Currie, Midlothian, and bound by James Burn at Esher, Surrey

I

'I'm giving you a splendid little class.' Blue eyes blinked up enthusiastically from a desk stacked with class registers and dinner money books.

'Thank you, Headmaster.'

I had taught at enough schools to make me suspect that the gift of a 'splendid little class' was not always a sacrifice. But this Headmaster had a blunt smile and guileless speech. He tripped my suspicions and sent them flying into the basement of trust.

'Come on,' he said, 'I'll take you to meet your class.'

We whisked through the swinging doors and down the windy corridors of Sunnyfield Modern Secondary School. There was a smell of chalk and wet raincoats and the school scuttled with first-day-of-term activity.

As we left the main building of the grey-stone town school we butted our heads against the driving rain and wind of January and ran across the sleek wet playground. In skirt and sweater, I felt that I was not properly dressed for a sprint. Mr Norris was small, white-haired and wiry as a harrier.

'You'll get used to this sort of thing in time,' shouted Mr Norris through the slashing rain. 'Moving from classroom to classroom gives a good chance of getting fresh air and exercise.'

I suspected that we also got a good chance of developing pneumonia, but that was before I discovered that self-preservation was the dominant theme of Sunnyfield.

We arrived at a building shaped roughly like a shoe box with a roof. Through the large classroom windows the restless shapes of children pulsated like tadpoles in a jar. The tadpoles caught sight of the Headmaster and, by the time we entered the classroom, the class was standing to ostentatious attention beside its desks.

There were forty eleven-year-old children. The boys were growing in or out of grey trousers and sweaters and the girls wore gymslips and blouses. They looked a pretty sturdy covey of unenlightenment and well able to resist eccentric onslaughts on their unblemished incomprehension.

The Headmaster broke the news that I was to be the new form mistress and would also attempt to teach English and Music. The children's eyes assessed and ran a mental measuring tape over me. No doubt they found me long and thin, like a whippet but with a less endearing personality.

'Wa-a-a-h!'

'Whe-e-e-e-e!'

'Go-r-r-r,' they breathed.

A teacher of English hadn't arrived a moment too soon. The Headmaster made a few remarks about the virtues of human charity and forbearance, to the children, then lifted off to his next appointment. I was alone with my class.

They remained standing. We stood face-to-face, the regulation stance for opponents in many trials of strength.

Suddenly I realised the enormity of my handicap. I was outnumbered by forty to one.

I had only one obvious advantage over the children. I was bigger than they were. In other schools I had taught classes of fourteen- and fifteen-year olds. I had forgotten that eleven-year-olds were, in comparison, still just Tots.

'Sit down, please,' I said and practically the whole class vanished from sight. Only a few heads, those of the taller of the Tots, appeared above the lids of the high desks. It was a disconcerting start. I had rehearsed a speech of welcome and togetherness for the class but I hesitated to make it to an almost invisible audience.

To gain time to think I droned through the register in the traditional manner, calling the girls by their Christian names and the boys by their surnames. The Tots responded according to their inclination.

'Jean' – 'Present Miss.'

'Linda' – 'Yes Miss.'

'Roberts' – 'O.K. Miss.'

'Rimmer' – 'Yah.'

'Sturgess' – 'Sright.'

As each Tot answered to its name it popped up from behind a raised desk lid, like a rabbit from its burrow on a fine day, then it went below again. The only Tots otherwise visible, were two lumpy boys who were holding a conversation while hanging head downward under their desks. It was a furtive form of talking in class which I had encountered before but under present conditions it was hopelessly conspicuous.

'What are you two talking about?' It was a purely

rhetorical question intended only to let the upended boys know that Miss was on the ball, but the Tots were a literal-minded lot.

'Talking about you, Miss.'

I was satisfied to leave the matter at that. Any teacher who worries around such a remark is very liable to find the tottering props of his self-confidence come crumbling in on him.

Children have an overweening regard for the truth and the Tots were no exception. They surfaced above the desk lids, their ears straining to catch the laugh-line. If I didn't follow through with the obvious line of enquiry I knew I would be in for a mettlesome round of 'playing up' in the near future. I decided to take a quick run at it.

'What were you saying about me?'

'You don't call the register right, Miss.'

'How do you mean?' I didn't know whether they expected me to sing it, chant it or make a production of it.

'You calls the girls by their Christian names but the boys by their surnames.'

'Isn't that the way most teachers call the register?'

'Yes, but us boys thinks it isn't right. We ought to be called by our Christian names, same as the girls. It's more friendly like.'

I was so relieved that the boys' remarks had so far steered me clear of humiliation that I was ready to bend over triangular to make myself agreeable.

'All right. I'll call the boys' names once again. Harold.'

There was no response.

'Harold who, Miss?' asked a sloe-eyed midget of a boy in the front row.

'Harold Frederick William Baxter, it says here in the register.'

'Oh, you means Old Basher, Miss.' The sloe-eyed one stood on one leg, and with a penknife, carefully scraped mud from his plimsolls.

'Do I? Stand up, Basher.'

A square boy with thick grey socks hoisted on white elastic bands scraped back his chair on the concrete floor and stood rolling his head in an embarrassed way. He was far larger than the average Tot and appeared to be about to burst from his jacket like a well-baked potato. I asked him if he wished to be called Harold. The square boy's ears blushed but he didn t reply.

'Yah. Call him Harold, Miss,' sniggered Mavis, a bossy, blonde girl who was sitting immediately in front of the boy.

Swiftly as the flick of a lizard's tongue, Harold's fist shot out and thumped Mavis in the back.

'Very well,' I said, 'Basher it will be.'

As I went through the register I found that there were very few boys in the class who were known by their Christian names. Most of them answered to nick-names. There was Toddy, Titch (of the sloe-eyes and plimsolls), Jobbo, Junky (whose father was a scrap-metal dealer), and a friendly dark-eyed boy, the build and colour of a short piece of string, who answered to the name of Sweet William. Titch explained that this was because Sweet William's father drove one of the tankers which did the essential work of clearing cess-pits in an area beyond the town boundary.

Titch was a talker and a speck of a boy whose main aim seemed to be making the most of himself longitudinally. He rarely sat down and, perhaps because he was so often handy on his feet, he had become spokesman for the class. This did not surprise me. I had often noticed that sitters tended to become comatose about the larynx.

When there was a chink in the barricade of Titch's chatter, Mavis edged in to tell me that there were urgent matters which required attention

'Dinner money's two and sevenpence short, Miss, and Tibby Maynard's mother's sent a note to say she thinks he's got yellow jaundice.'

I hadn't had much truck with jaundice so I tackled the problem of the dinner money. Mavis volunteered to re-check the pile of money on my desk while I totalled the amounts in the book. I added up three times and each time got a different answer.

Titch, his grey plimsolled feet itching with curiosity, weaved and circled around my desk like a boxer anxious not to let his footwork run to waste.

'You ain't much good at sums, are you, Miss?' he said.

'No.' Lies were pointless. I realised that, given time, the Tots would plumb the depths of all my inadequacies.

'Chuck the dinner money book over here, Miss,' said Titch, magnanimously, 'I'll check it for you.'

I hesitated but the rest of the Tots had no doubts as to Titch's ability.

'Go on, Miss. Let Titch do it. He's good at sums. Always gets top marks in arithmetic.'

Everyone was silent while Titch, the Arithmetical

Wonder, fell to the addition and came up with the correct answer. The Tots were proud of Titch.

'Worked out a perm for his Dad on the football pools, Miss, Titch did. He'll work out a perm for you, Miss, if you like.'

I didn't know whether I ought to congratulate Titch, accept his offer, or give him a talk on the evils of gambling. Luckily I was spared the choice. The school bell rang for morning Assembly. The Tots fell into a flurry of desk-lid banging, book collecting and preparation. Mavis took a comb and mirror from her desk. She thoughtfully arranged her long hair, flicked a wet finger over a self-possessed eyebrow and announced that she was ready to pray.

'Pray?'

'Yes, Miss. In Assembly every morning we pray. Sometimes it's for the United Nations, sometimes it's for people who don't get enough to eat. Last week we put in a word for the new school piano but it hasn't arrived yet.'

'Here's your hymn book, Miss,' said Dinny, a dark-haired earnest girl who was Mavis's aide-de-camp. Dinny flicked over me her disapproving glance. On closer acquaintance I found that Dinny had much to commend her, but she had about her a serious mein which nipped all folly in the bud. Only Mavis, with her ebullient audacity, could support Dinny as a friend. Mavis had the ability to laugh off Dinny's predilection for doom and belief in the darker hints contained in her newspaper horoscope.

Dinny put into my hand an ink-stained book covering and a few loose pages.

'If the Headmaster chooses a hymn that's missing in your

book and you don't know the words, just mime it, Miss,' Dinny seriously advised. 'Mavis and me, we mimed "He Who Would Valiant Be" lovely last term. Didn't we, Mave?'

But Mavis was busy shepherding the Tots into a straight line and marching them across the playground.

'Left, right, heads up, keep in line. That's right,' shouted Mavis as she followed the squad. Dinny, with a formidable array of pens and pencils clipped around the neckline of her gymslip, brought up the rear.

I sprinted after the marching column of Tots, vainly trying to regain some authority over the tramping column as it bore straight across the puddled playground, up a flight of stairs, through a science laboratory and finally crashed its way into a packed School Hall.

It was, perhaps, as well that not everyone in the Hall cared to sing because there was not sufficient room for everyone to take in the necessary breath. The Hall had been designed for far fewer children than the hundreds who now jammed into it.

With the rest of the staff, I stood on the narrow wedge of board called 'the stage.' Mr Norris, the Headmaster, prayed, sang and gave out the football results beautifully. He said that we should all pull together. Then we prayed. That morning it was for strength to face the coming term. The Tots, who seemed to have their eyes on me, were very earnest about it and, at the end, sent up a loud 'Amen.'

The opening chords of 'He Who Would Valiant Be' were struck on the piano. I opened my hymn book and found the page of that hymn missing. I managed for a while then ran

woman approaching middle age, she taught every class of girls in the school and shuttled backwards and forwards between the Games Field and the Gym from Monday morning to Friday night. She had not one break long enough to change her socks or catch her breath. Her lunch hour she used to train hockey and netball teams, after school every evening she held practice matches and on Saturdays she refereed home and away matches. Apart from that her time was her own. Miss Slater was a hard act to follow, even if you had talent and muscles, and I had neither.

When I called the Tots' register the next morning I was wearing shorts and sweater.

'Wa-a-a-ah, Miss,' gasped Mavis, 'we never thought you was a Games Teacher.'

I didn't tell Mavis that I too had never thought I was. However, I found that just having the outward toggery of a games teacher can bestow upon almost anyone the accolade of popularity. And having so many children *like* you, abruptly, can throw all psychological reflexes into a pretty tangle. It was difficult to become used to teaching a subject which children enjoyed learning.

My first P.T. class was a group of fifteen-year-old girls. I had a notion that a teacher should promote in her pupils a feeling of mutual confidence. After some warming-up exercises we got out the 'horse' and fixed it on its shortest legs. I lurched over it but the girls were not impressed. They said they were accustomed to jumping much higher so they raised the legs a few notches.

'Over you go,' I shouted encouragingly and, to make quite certain there would be no possibility of my having to demonstrate the leap at this higher altitude, I made myself one of the catchers. There is more to teaching than imparting knowledge. Sometimes outright chicanery is necessary and, with that said, it has to be admitted that it can still too often be a job which presents its implacable North face.

We were nearing the end of the lesson when the girls asked if they might play a game of Shipwreck. I didn't know what Shipwreck was, as a game. In my book 'Shipwreck' was something unpleasant, exhausting and liable to prove fatal. Perhaps it would have been as well if I had retained that notion. However, the girls said they always played Shipwreck with the indefatigable Miss Slater so I agreed that they should teach me the game.

They arranged around the perimeter of the room all the equipment: forms, boxes, buck, horse, etc. Then each player perched herself on a piece of equipment. The game of Shipwreck was like musical chairs. When the music began the players moved around the room and one piece of furniture was removed. When the music stopped players had to clamber aboard a 'Ship' and anyone with as much as a small toe on the ground had to leave the game. The last person left 'Aboard' was the winner.

It sounded like a good idea. All I had to do was to blow a whistle, and that, requiring a shallow brain and deep lungs, I thought I might manage. Unfortunately, in the second game, the girls insisted that I should not be denied the pleasure of joining in the game, as Miss Slater did.

After a few minutes of Shipwreck I would have given a lot to have been drowned at sea. I felt breathless, bruised and grazed. I dearly wanted to be caught 'out' and all that kept me upright was a lack of proper humility and a few overheard ribald remarks.

The lesson over, I tottered, exhausted and gasping, to change into my track suit for Games. Mr Norris swept out of his study, his secretary close at his heels.

'You're doing fine,' he shouted as he whirled past me. 'Hurry up now. Your Games class is waiting. You will enjoy a brisk game of hockey.'

I wanted to ask if there was anywhere where I might lie down and die for half an hour, but I didn't dare. I knew what the answer would be.

'Miss Slater never did.'

I was reasonably sure that Games lessons would be easier than teaching P.T. I would arrange a game of hockey or netball, blow the starter's whistle and let the girls loose to enjoy themselves. I would flounder about the pitch, obstruct play and prove that as a referee I was active, if inept. It would be easy to sneak a look at the book of rules and occasionally blow my whistle for a penalty or free shot or some such thing, and prove that in all alleys of life I favoured a rough approach to the morality of the Queensberry rules.

In any one class there were rarely the exact number of players required for the games. There were too many girls or not enough. I supposed that Miss Slater had overcome the difficulty by playing all missing positions herself and refereeing the game.

I was less energetic so I had to be resourceful. I changed the rules of the games, temporarily, to suit the number of players available. It made for exciting, if controversial, contests. The impromptu rules went well with the team which happened to gain by them but brought yells of protest from the opposing side. If I wasn't on the games pitch to pronounce a (probably unjust) decision on behalf of the plaintiffs or the defendants the row often ended in scuffles and the sort of word-slinging which I wished I could not overhear from the adjoining pitch.

'Her rules is daft.'

'Well, she says we got to play by them.'

'She's potty. Miss Slater never changed the rules.'

The efficiency of Miss Slater reached out to slur my good intentions, even as she tossed on her bed of sickness.

When there were too many girls for the teams the problem was what to do with the 'left-overs.' If I left them to practise tactics on their own they soon lost interest. And as there were two or three games in progress I had to keep an eye on all groups to see that they became neither too fractious nor too lethargic. Finally I settled for dashing from group to group trying to restore order and interest. I felt like one of those variety turns who has to keep himself and a row of spinning plates in a state of perpetual motion.

Like most Games Teachers, I feared rain worse than fallen arches. One of the advantages of Games and P.T. lessons at a school so bulging with pupils as Sunnyfield was that they relieved the demand for classroom space. When it rained Games groups wandered around the school looking like tribes who had just missed the last bus to their particular Valhalla. Mr Critchley, the boys' P.T. and Games master, and I, took our sports-deprived classes into the Gym and tried to placate them.

Mr Critchley was built like a block of flats, from the solid foundation of his large feet to the fair hair which topped his bland face like a polar ice-cap. His outward torpor was deceptive. Given the incentive, his feet and wits were supersonic and his voice, when giving commands, had a resonant quality which infiltrated into every classroom and overthrew more subversive cults than we cared to admit.

Country Dancing was an activity which placated the girls but incensed the boys. Boys were coerced into dancing with girls only under duress. The boys glowered and muttered throughout the dance and clomped in an anti-clockwise direction when the dance-figure demanded everyone moving clockwise. These counter-revolutions caused as many cracked skulls and requests for sticking plaster as a minor insurrection.

If Basher was in the class I had to watch him carefully or he would 'accidentally' bump into the record player and jerk the needle to skip a few grooves of the record. Then we might find ourselves dancing the last figure of a Polish mazurka to the opening bars of the Gay Gordons. It did make a difference, to anyone who cared.

Shipwreck pleased both boys and girls. With twice the usual number of players there was rowdy competition for possession of the 'islands' and when I felt that the going might be too rough for the girls I said that any of them who wished might stand out.

The girls regretted me with a look and not one of them budged. The music started and they pitched into the scrimmage. Sometimes I despaired of our turning out sweet, feminine creatures from Sunnyfield but I need not have worried. In time, nature did it for us. The top forms were full of prospective carnival and beauty queens. They made early marriages, in white, and with sheaves of brides-maids. I never heard of one of them coming to what I once heard a Needlework Mistress describe as 'a sticky end.' Shipwreck, perhaps, was a good training for life.

Teaching Games and P.T. certainly prepared me for something. I had to be as obdurate in that belief as in the application of liniment or I could not have carried on with what seemed at best a bootless form of affliction. When a Supply Teacher arrived to take over Miss Slater's work I stood down, creaking and thankful.

The next morning, fully dressed, I faced the Tots. They looked disappointed that I no longer appeared in shorts, track suit or other forms of fancy dress.

'W-a-a-ah, Miss,' said Mavis. 'We thought you was a Games Teacher.'

'Red Riding Hood thought the wolf was her granny,' I said. 'Get out your English books and turn to page eighteen.'

I eased myself into a perch on top of my desk, where I had a good view over the class. A teacher of English, I thought, might be less popular than a Games Mistress but at least she got to have a sit down once in a while.

III

The Tots and I renewed our sagging acquaintance and I began to learn their idiosyncrasies. One of these was a built-in habit which the Tots called 'Doing Library.'

Left to their own devices for a few minutes while I answered a message or totalled a register, the children disappeared beneath their desk-lids, popped up with film and pop-star annuals, comics and educationally unsuitable paperbacks and an absorbed and uncanny silence fell.

I enquired what they were doing and Mavis whispered (no doubt on account of the solemnity of the occasion), 'We're Doing Library, Miss.'

I walked around the class and took a closer look at the 'Library' books. They ranged from seed catalogues and mail order books to back numbers of magazines whose photographs catered for the sexually unenlightened.

'Haven't you any proper Library books?' I asked.

Dinny looked up from reading a heart-warming magazine story. Dinny rejoiced in true tales of others' anguish which promoted a smug aura of self-satisfaction in the reader.

'These are our Library books, Miss. We swop with each other, see?'

Suddenly I felt a great compassion for the Tots and their lack of 'good' literature.

'How would you like it if we had *real* Library books?' I asked, impulsively. I had no idea where I was going to find sufficient books for a Library for forty children but I felt that I must, if only to see Dinny's sweetly serious face unmanned by a book of comic verse.

'Oooh, yes, Miss.' The Tots sat up in their desks, spry as sparrows. Only Dinny had reservations. She looked at me gravely, as if she were about to impart to me the perfidies of this planet.

'My sister had a book out of the Public Library once, Miss, and it didn't have not one picture!'

This news fell like a collapsing ideological block and tackle on the Tot's ideas of the fitness of things. I hastened to shore up their illusions. I didn't want Dinny promoting a morbid funk of the printed page and a return to the pre-glacial culture of the comic strip.

We decided to provide a Library for ourselves. I collected together all the suitable books I had and bought some children's paperbacks but we still had nowhere near enough books. We needed money to buy books.

'Have a raffle,' suggested Mavis. 'A shilling a ticket for a transistor radio.'

I said I didn't have a transistor or know anyone willing to give one.

'Bingo,' said Junky, leaning over the front of my desk and wagging a solemn grimy finger in my face. Junky had red hair which, in times of deliberation such as now, stood up on his forehead like an affronted toothbrush. He screwed up his lids over his green-flecked eyes and gave me his confidence.

'There's a lot of money to be made, Miss, in organising Bingo.'

I didn't know how the Headmaster or the parents would regard gambling among the Tots. I decided I had better stick to something safer, even if financially less rewarding.

'A Lucky Dip,' I said. 'I'll put wrapped presents in a barrel of sawdust and we can have a gift for sixpence a go.'

'A bob, Miss,' argued Junky. 'Make 'em pay.'

'I think sixpence will be enough, Junky.'

I collected together my unused Christmas and birthday gifts of handkerchiefs, bath salts, soap and perfume, but finding presents for the boys was more difficult. I had to reject an offer of packets of razor blades but accepted a kaleidoscopic beach shirt (small size), sun spectacles, unused business diaries and several pocket compasses.

After school on Friday evening the Tots lined up to have a go at the Lucky Dip. Children from other forms crowded outside the classroom and peered through the windows. I promised that, if there were any gifts over, they also might have a turn.

Mavis was first in the queue. She put her hand into the barrel of sawdust (which the boys had collected from the Woodwork Room). She unwrapped her gift, which was a bottle of cheap perfume.

'Wa-a-a-ah, Miss! Scent.' Mavis unstoppered the bottle and poured perfume lavishly over herself.

'Lovely, Miss. Smell.' Mavis anointed Dinny and two of her special friends and Titch immediately jumped on his desk and opened a window, very wide.

'Pongs,' complained Basher as he dipped into the barrel and brought up his gift. It was a pocket compass.

'Caw! A compass!' he whooped. The rest of the boys crowded around Basher excitedly.

'What you want a compass for?' asked Dinny.

'Well,' said Basher, 'you can tell which way you're going – when you're escaping through jungles and things.'

The boys awaiting their turn at the barrel elbowed for a better position. They wanted to know if there were any more compasses. Evidently they were all keen on escaping from jungles.

The Lucky Dip was being a great success and some Tots were queuing for a second turn when disaster struck.

'I've got soap,' said Junky, staring incredulously at the pink tablet which he had unwrapped.

'A tanner, and I got soap!' Junky was never one for as much as a rearguard action in the forward march of hygiene. As the son of a junk-collector, he was proud heir to a certain amount of acceptance in the way of honest grime. He saw no reason to trouble his head, or any other part of his fabric, with pink soap.

He cheered up when one of the girls swopped the soap for a calendar. He pinned it on the classroom wall and it became known as Junky's Calendar. Each morning Junky, and he alone, crossed off a day in thick black crayon. The calendar was not as ostentatious or dramatic a gift as a compass but it carried with it ceremonial privileges which increased Junky's prestige and did more for his ego than a bar of soap.

By the time the school bus left that evening the classroom floor was sprinkled with sawdust, a lapse which would need some explaining to Mr Hibberd, the school caretaker. My spirit stood cap in hand before Mr Hibberd's trenchant notes about apple cores left in the waste-paper basket. Some Tots would get up half an hour early for the pleasure of reading one of Mr Hibberd's open letters to 'Miss' often left on my desk. The notes were accompanied by repudiated half-chewed toffees, fusty apples or whatever happened not to fit in with Mr Hibberd's refuse arrangements for that day. The notes were not intended to curry favour with me but they started off the day for the Tots with a cheerful and harmless faith in retributive justice.

On Saturday morning I took three Tot-elected choosers of Library books (Mavis, Junky and Titch) to the bookshop in town to spend the money we had collected.

'They got walls made of books,' said Titch, flinging himself into the air to take a look at the higher shelves.

Mavis had to be dissuaded from buying an entire collection of books about horses, Titch wanted nothing but science fiction and Junky, the good marketer of the party, looked for bargains in the second-hand book stock.

On Monday morning the books were arranged on the shelves of a small classroom cupboard and marked, very importantly, 'Library.'

The Library was opened officially after lunch and some of the Tots skipped their pudding (prunes and custard, which they considered no loss except to the grocery trade) to be first under starter's orders at the Library cupboard.

Forty Tots wrestling to get into a cupboard about the size of a small larder was a situation which I had not foreseen. Those inside were fighting to get out with their chosen books and those outside were screeching to be let in. I thought that someone might be hurt so I yelled at them to simmer down but my voice was lost in the pandemonium. I tried to get into the cupboard to help out those trapped but someone, thinking I was trying to get a book out of turn, gave me a sharp kick on the ankle. The someone said 'Sorry, Miss,' but as the kick and the apology were delivered together I was left to draw my own conclusions.

Eventually I eased myself into the cupboard but found that the expiring Tots had escaped by crawling between the legs of the in-going army. The escapers were now outside the cupboard and signalling to me that they wanted their Library books checked out.

Mr Norris swept past the window and I shouted to him for help. He looked in, gave me an encouraging smile and wave, and went on his way. He liked to see the Tots being active and using their initiative. He had no idea what we were doing but, seeing their teacher in their midst, he assumed that the Tots were having some healthy lunch-hour free discipline.

There was nothing else to do. I reached for my P.T. whistle and blasted the Tots into silence. I walked from the cupboard unscathed and hoped that my silence conveyed to the Tots my disapproval of their behaviour. But it didn't. To the Tots the sound of the whistle had only one meaning.

'C-a-aw! Shipwreck,' said Mavis. Forgetting their Library books, the Tots jumped on desks, chairs, window-ledges, waste-paper baskets and hot-water pipes.

'Smashing, Miss,' said Junky. 'We knew you wasn't going to be a stuffy old English teacher. Not for always!'

IV

The Tots jostled and butted each other in their eagerness to get into Music classes. This was not due to any unwarranted musical sensibility but to the fact that first comers claimed the seats in the back row. There, removed from 'Miss,' the non-vocal singers hoped to escape detection.

In other lessons it was possible to walk around the classroom but for a part of the Music lesson I was anchored to the piano. This time was acknowledged to be favourable for a bit of resolute inertia, vegetative cleaning of the finger nails with the point of a compass and other forms of determined sloth.

One day I found what I hoped was a resourceful method of dealing with the problem.

'Back row change places with front row.'

'But, Miss, we queued up for these seats.' A chorus went up from the aggrieved back row. 'It's not fair,' they grumbled audibly as they moved their things to the front. The children in the front row also grumbled because, strangely enough, they liked being in the front row. They were the Tots who were good at sight-reading or liked singing. Sometimes they were children who liked to 'show off' so an occasional change of position did their ego no harm.

After I had surprised the class with the reversal act several times I came to be regarded by the back-benchers as 'unreliable' and moreover a bit 'dotty.' Instead of fighting for back-row positions before Music lessons the Tots spent their time in betting (anything from a penny to an old comic) whether the lesson would be a normal or a 'flip-side' affair. The regular back-row boys now took no chances. They sat in the middle of the classroom where they mouthed the words of 'Three jolly sailor boys' soundlessly, as usual.

It was necessary to take some kind of a stand in the cause of audible singing. I picked out several of the 'mutes' and asked them to sing together a song which the class had been learning, painfully, for months. I led with the introduction at the piano, but from the boys there was silence.

'I don't hear a sound,' I said.

'No, Miss. We got broke voices.'

'All of you?'

'Yes, Miss. I reckon it's catching, see.'

I didn't see but when I remembered the sound of the 'broke' voices when 'whole' I felt a justified gratitude.

Despite the 'growlers' Music lessons were sometimes almost enjoyable. When it was learned that I didn't expect a high degree of musicianship but was grateful merely for an appreciation of music there was an immediate and good-hearted response. I felt like a radio disc-jockey who had let his fans into the studio.

'Let's have that record of "Orphans in the Underground",' the request-Tots yelled.

'Nah. We wants the "Sorterer's Apprentice," Miss,' chanted the Opposition.

Most Tots didn't care which record was played as long as they had nothing to do but sit back and 'appreciate.' When I dared to ask Mavis if she knew which instrument had opened a particular theme she looked at me reproachfully.

'I don't know, Miss. I wasn't thinking of things like that. I was appreciating the music.'

It was a long time before the Tots realised that 'appreciating' music did not prevent them from listening to it.

Sight-reading was a part of the Music lesson which the Tots did reluctantly, all except a determined squat boy named Toddy who at all times carried a pencil behind his ear and a ruler inside the leg of one sock. These gave Toddy a strangely inquiring inclination of the head and a rigidity of one leg, which made him look as if he were constantly in search of the Outpatients' Department.

As soon as sight-reading books were given out Toddy put up his hand and asked to go to the lavatory. It was a request which I did not like to refuse. So, while the class got on with the sight-reading, I watched Toddy making his way across the playground, in the circumstances very slowly, I thought. Toddy didn't emerge until sight-reading was over and he heard the Tots taking a good belt at 'Non Nobis.'

This was a song the words of which few Tots understood but which was full of good long notes, and the Tots dearly loved a good note. Once found and held, they hated to part with it. Mavis and Dinny often held the final note of 'Non Nobis' almost until the books had been collected and the first straw was gurgling in the mid-morning milk.

Singing occupied a great deal of our time at Sunnyfield. In the morning in Assembly we polished off a few hymns and from the Music Room there was the daily wail of jolly dirges. After school hours staff and pupils got together and bawled out a few songs from the production which the School Musical Society were 'doing' that term. And once Sunnyfield had 'done' a particular work its sales of sheet music in the district could expect to plummet for several years.

The singing at Sunnyfield had more of quantity than quality, and it was difficult to improve this situation The impression was that singing 'came naturally,' more often than not while in the bath, therefore it needed no skill or practice, only the prompting of a rough loofah and a cold tap.

With the Tots I reversed the order of things and taught them how *not* to sing. I imitated a few of the ways in which the voice should not be produced, the nasal tone, the 'breathy' tone etc. The imitation the Tots enjoyed most was called 'The Throaty Tenor.' When there was time to spare at the end of a Music lesson, the Tots often requested, 'Do the Throaty Tenor, Miss.' They preferred seeing 'Miss' standing up making a fool of herself to a few bars of 'Underground Orphans.' The Throaty Tenor became a well-known comedy act and during lunch-hour I would often hear imitations of my imitation echoing across the playground.

At the time when the Throaty Tenor was Top of the Playground Pops, the Sunnyfield Choral Society plunged into its latest production. The Tots learned their parts, then everyone met in the School Hall to do battle; sopranos v. altos, baritones v. tenors etc. The Tots were unconvinced that musical parts were written to complement each other. The children were so inured to the competitive spirit in all facets of school life that when they were picked for musical parts they thought that they had to fight, vocally, for their 'side.' In this production the altos had a particularly puny line so I sat in with them to help them hold their own.

The solo parts were taken by local amateurs and, when the Tots and the Big Uns had learned their parts as well as ever they were likely to, we crammed ourselves on to the school stage and had our first rehearsal.

The Tots had been told that they must sit still during the solos and, during the first run-through, I felt very proud of them. If their singing left something to be desired, at least they sat well. They were so fascinated by the soloists that they completely forgot to fidget. The soprano was a pretty girl with a delightful voice, and some of the older boys whispered during her applause, 'Isn't she smashing, Miss?'

When the opening bars of the tenor solo were played we settled down for another few minutes of listening. A clerical-looking young man, still wearing cycling clips, stood up and before he had sung more than a few plummy notes every child on the stage turned to me and grinned. The singer was the Throaty Tenor to the larynx.

I tried to avoid the bright eyes expecting my acknowledgment of the joke for if there is one thing adults in a school must do it is to remain indivisible. I pretended to be deaf to the giggles and nudges all round me and looked fixedly at the wall.

When the song was over I applauded and the Tots, thinking that 'Miss' had at times a perverse sense of humour, clapped, stamped on the floor and demanded an encore. The bicycle clips quivered with pleasure. I felt almost ashamed.

'Such very pleasant children,' the tenor said after the rehearsal. 'Teaching them must be a very rewarding occupation.'

'Oh, yes,' I agreed. I didn't tell him that the rewards often recoiled on my head in a way which served me right.

V

During the windy days of March the Tots grew restless and disinterested in lessons. The rest of the staff said that their classes were also turbulent and that it was one of the strange effects on children of boisterous weather, so I didn't worry unduly. Then I discovered that my class had an additional reason for their unco-operative behaviour. The Tots bore me a small grudge over the business of the desks.

At the start of term I spoke to Mr Norris about the desks being too large for most of the Tots.

'Order smaller desks for those children who need them,' he said.

I had not realised that educational small-beer such as I had the authority to order so much as a pencil sharpener. The notion of commanding, with the Headmaster's backing, the delivery of pounds' worth of brand new desks brought me out in a rash of benefaction. The Tots found the news heady stuff for their ego and told the rest of the school that they were to have desks designed especially for them and the desks would arrive 'any day now.'

The quoted phrase was mine. 'Any day now' was the answer I gave when a Tot, toppled off a precarious perch of a pile of books on his chair, picked himself up and demanded to know when the new desks would arrive. I gave the same answer to the boy who sat on his satchel to gain elevation and gained only milk-break sandwiches flattened to a wafer.

On similar trying occasions lessons would be halted while we discussed the new desks and drooled in anticipation of the day they would arrive. The sound of a coal or milk lorry in the playground sent the Tots scudding to the windows to see if it might be the new desks arriving.

'Those new desks are a fixation with your little lot,' said Pinks Thomson, the Science master. Pinks was a bear-shaped, volatile man who gave me plenty of good advice, perhaps more than he could safely spare. He needed all the sagacity he could muster to get through each day unscathed. His laboratory experiments and his sports jackets were often of an explosive nature. The dull edge of many a day at Sunnyfield was honed with the sight of Pinks hurrying across the quadrangle with red fire extinguisher clasped to his checkerboard tweed.

'Your little lot,' said Pinks, deftly slotting a newly charged fire extinguisher home, 'they brag to the other kids. Say you ordered the desks by their measurements. You'd think, to hear them talk, that the desks were bespoke. Do you know how long it sometimes takes for these orders to arrive? I think you will be very lucky if you see those desks this side of the Summer holidays.'

I knew that Pinks spoke the truth. A man with his response to colour preferred the gaudy fabric of truth to any white lie.

I thought of warning the Tots that the desks might

be late in arriving but, as I wasn't absolutely sure about this, I decided to say nothing. The promise of new desks had prodded me into an unexpected position of prestige with the Tots. A 'Miss' who could produce, or promise to produce, about thirty new desks at the drop of a ruler seemed almost as good as a Games teacher.

Throughout January and February the Tots willingly dragged their chairs into the aisles so that they could read the blackboard, and when they had to write at their desks, the smallest readily climbed on boxes just for the un-accustomed pleasure of propping their elbows on the desk.

I rode a wave of goodwill but as each day passed my surf-board grew shakier. I questioned Pinks again as to how long orders took in arriving but he was vague. I think he was so addicted to living on a plane of momentary mortality that it was difficult for him to think in terms of protracted time.

The term trickled by and the Tots, aloft on books and biscuit tins, grew uncomfortable and plaintive. Word seeped through to them that there was a niggling doubt about the delivery date of the desks. The myth of the omnipotent 'Miss' faded and the dry rot of doubt set in. The Tots began to doubt the truth of any statement I made to them and dealing with forty confirmed disbelievers was difficult.

'John Bunyan wrote "Pilgrim's Progress".'

'How do you know for sure, Miss?' enquired Titch, one of the leaders of the Sceptical Revival. 'You didn't actually see him write it, did you, so you can't be sure, can you, Miss?' From the Tots there was a murmur of assent at this piece of shaky logic.

As each day of non-delivery of the desks passed the Tots questioned each slice of information I handed them, from the name of the Prime Minister to the day of the week. The desks were never alluded to but I knew that the Tots held me responsible for setting them up as Aunt Sallys for the jeers of the school.

I had no more volunteers to clean the blackboard and those Tots whom I pressed into this service did it with an unnecessary vigour which covered me in clouds of chalk dust. I became the dustiest and most miserable teacher in the school.

Then, by accident, I discovered a way in which I might creep back into the Tots' good books. It needed endurance but I determined to try it.

One of the most well-meaning members of staff was a Mr Gideon, a quiet young man with an unlimited supply of tolerance. A lack of hardness of heart was, as a teacher, his corrupting virtue. He had little class discipline so he was baited and plagued unmercifully. We would often hear from our classroom classes in full cry as they 'playcd old Giddy up.'

Yet in the School Dining Hall one lunch-hour I heard the Big Uns and the Tots shouting in opposition for the pleasure of having Giddy eat at their table. To be invited by children to dine with them indicated that a teacher was a favourite. Mr Gideon sat at the head of the Tots' table, a gentle smile lapping the corners of his mouth and his dark-spectacled blue eyes blinking in the sudden glint of unaccustomed courtesy.

It was an affecting sight, invoking tears and suspicion.

Without being invited I sat at the other end of the table and, looking around, gave what I hoped was a 'I know what you're up to' look. The Tots were not in the least abashed. While I ate my dinner they turned their charms on Giddy. I kept my ears beamed in on the conversation, which seemed harmless enough. I began to think that I had misjudged the Tots. They were truly sorry for making his flesh heir to more troubles than a knockabout patsy. They were penitent. Tears almost came to my eyes as I choked back a forkful of cold mashed potato.

I glanced up to see how Giddy was bearing up under the strain of the Tots' sudden conversion and realised that he was not eating. A basin of ginger pudding arrived for the table and Giddy refused his helping. Dinny, who was in charge of serving, divided Giddy's portion into four and the Tots chosen by her held out their plates for 'extras.' My illusions instantly wilted and in their place misgiving burgeoned.

Mr Gideon and I strolled back to our classrooms. He looked far happier than I had ever seen him in school hours.

'I'm on a diet,' he confided. 'Ulcer, you know. I'm not allowed to eat certain things. I wouldn't bother going to the Dining Hall at all but your class have invited me to sit with them and I don't like to disappoint them.'

I didn't tell Giddy that the Tots had by now probably worked out a sharing roster for his dinners for the next two or three years. He was so content in his new-found popularity, that, despite the ulcer, he looked well.

The next day I dined, unrequested, at the Tots' table. Mrs

Williams, the school cook, had made steak and kidney pie. It arrived at table looking as delicious as it always tasted. Before the savoury smell frayed my resolution I said loudly, 'None for me, thank you. I'll have only a little cabbage.'

The Tots' heads swivelled to my end of the table and forty pairs of incredulous eyes met mine. I stared back, trying to put on a bland look, as if I had just taken vows of gastronomic temperance. Seeing I was not joking, the Tots swiftly divided the pie and downed it before I could change my mind.

'You not feeling well, Miss?' Mavis enquired.

'Quite well, thank you, Mavis. I'm slimming.'

Knives and forks halted in mid-air. Jaws dropped under the combined weight of steak and kidney and horror. The idea of a 'Miss' who already looked like a yard of narrow elastic getting any thinner stirred panic even among the most case-hardened 'H' film addicts. Some of the Tots seemed about to protest when they saw the baked apples and custard for 'afters' and decided that extra rations were as good a nerve-tonic as anything.

The following day I refused treacle tart, the next fish pie (which was not such a sacrifice) and by the end of the week I was the most sought-after dinner guest in the school, and the hungriest. In order to refuse food I brought sandwiches which I bolted secretly in the Games equipment cupboard before going into the Dining Hall.

The flesh began to hang upon my bones but, as far as the Tots were concerned, I was the most popular skinny teacher ever. They forgot their discontent over the matter of the desks and I wallowed in their well-fed benevolence. The

Tots' behaviour was exemplary and improbable. I actually saw Basher cuffing Toddy for not 'paying attention to Miss.' The pencil whizzed from behind Toddy's ear, upsetting his equilibrium for the whole afternoon.

'If you don't watch out,' Basher said, 'she won't sit with us and it's my turn for extras.'

'Don't care,' said Toddy, who was always very edgy when suddenly pencil-less and reverted to normal plumb. 'It's rice pudding tomorrow and I don't like rice pudding.' Toddy replaced the pencil and his usual lop-sided dignity.

'Don't like rice pudding? Why didn't you say so before?' Basher gave Toddy a second cuff but this time it was more of a gentle pat of approval and the pencil hardly fluttered behind Toddy's ear. Basher leaned back in his chair, thinking that two portions of rice pudding were even better than one.

When food was in view Giddy and I were the most popular teachers in school. We had dinner invitations booked weeks in advance. Giddy, still unaware of the reason for our being in favour, began to recover his health and his appetite. His doctor said that he might relax his diet and I looked on helplessly and enviously as he tucked into his first school dinner. Requests for his company no longer echoed above the clatter of the plates and each day the noise of insurrection grew louder from his classroom.

My telling Giddy the truth would have been pointless and unkind. Such was the incredible innocence of the man that he would not have believed me. His case was a salutary warning to me whenever I felt like taking a ravenous run at a school dinner.

Then, one day just before the school bell rang for lunch-hour, a large van lurched over the pot-holes on the edges of the playground. The truck driver parked it near our classroom and came in to ask the way to the Headmaster's room. He said there was a delivery note to be signed.

'It isn't, by any chance, a consignment of new desks?'

'That's right.'

When the bell rang the Tots rushed into the playground to supervise the unloading of their new desks. They were of the latest design and the correct size. By the afternoon the desks were installed in the classroom and the Tots smugly installed in the desks.

'Some people,' said Mavis, giving her blonde head a gesture of authority – 'when some people in this school see these desks they will have to eat their words.'

I looked forward to a more substantial diet, at last!

VI

The Tots had a weakness for anything dumb on four legs and, after teaching the Tots, I too began to find brute silence very appealing. Nevertheless, it seemed reasonable to prohibit animals in the classroom, after I had met Caper.

One day a terrier-type dog in Brand X off-white and dusty black sat slummocky on one haunch in the aisle between the Tots' desks. With his head cocked on one side he listened gravely while I gave an account of the work of the verb. The animal was attentive but I felt there was something slightly ridiculous in lecturing to a patch-eyed mongrel.

'What is that animal doing here?' I asked.

'That's Caper, Junky's dog,' said Basher. 'He's all right. Caper won't hurt you, Miss.'

Caper lifted a gawky flank and scratched himself behind an off-white ear.

'I know the dog won't hurt me, but what is it *doing* here?'

'Please, Miss. Caper come to school with me,' said Junky. 'He usually stays home with my Mum but Caper come with me today because my Mum's hurt Caper's feelings. She *hit* him, real hard.'

From the Tots there was a chorus of sympathy for Caper.

The dog's beseeching eyes leered around the class. I too felt a reluctant pity for the animal.

'Why did your mother hit – er – Caper?'

'No reason, Miss. Caper never done nothing much. He only took the Sunday joint from the kitchen table on Sunday morning – took it into the garden and ate it. It was just Caper's fun. But my Mum chased Caper with a tennis racquet and she *hit* him.'

I realised why the animal was so docile and content to sit about doing nothing. After eating a family's Sunday dinner, on Monday anything more energetic than digestion was probably impossible. But Caper could go and digest his joint elsewhere. I knew Junky couldn't take the dog home until the end of the day because they lived miles away and travelled by school bus.

'Take the animal outside the classroom,' I said.

Junky took Caper by the collar and led the dog outside, to the muttered protests of the Tots, whose opinion it was that Caper was 'not doing no harm.' I couldn't prove otherwise so I felt a bit like the wicked stepmother. The only consolation I had was that I was doing the correct thing, a thought which at best made me feel no more than pompous. The thought of Caper sitting sadly outside the classroom door made me feel unjust. I resented feeling a psychiatrist's couch-load of guilt just because I had denied an unkempt mongrel the opportunity of learning about the verb. True the dog could gain nothing from the lesson but, by the same token, the same thing might be said of some of the Tots.

After the English lesson was over the Tots and I remained

43

in the classroom for Music. In the break between lessons I weakened enough to let Junky go outside and see if Caper was all right. I made it sound as if I were doing Junky a favour but in truth I didn t want it on my conscience if the dog wandered off and was run over.

'Caper's O.K., Miss,' said Junky. 'He's sitting under the window. He won't go away.'

Often, teaching the Tots could be a pleasure, and so it was that Music lesson, or almost. The Tots enjoyed any lesson with plenty of audience-participation and noise, so Music suited their talents admirably.

In sight-reading the Tots were not backward in pitching notes. The notes were many, varied and usually inaccurate. However, when it came to singing a tune which they knew, no more enthusiastic choir existed than the Tots. A song which they enjoyed was one about Peaceful Wales, with Mavis singing the solo. Mavis's voice soared and was joined by a mournful yowl of random pitch. Caper, sitting below the open window, wailed his way through the rest of the song.

'Caper's very fond of a bit of music,' Junky said. 'I reckon Caper's the most musical dog ever. He loves to sing if there's a good tune on the radio.'

After that nothing would do but that Caper, the Musical Dog, should come into the classroom and join in the music-making. The Tots held that I couldn't rightly refuse admission to a music-lover, even if canine, and so it was that morning that the song about Peaceful Wales sounded less peaceful than usual.

My paying any attention to Caper's musical abilities was

a mistake. After the Caper incident Tot after Tot turned up at school with a pet in tow. There were dogs which barked to records of brass bands, poodles which dressed in red jersey and tea-cosy hats, a cat which played ping-pong and a smooth-haired terrier which stood on its hind legs and nodded a football about. We spent so much time watching performing animals that my register was rarely completed on time and dinner-money collecting was always late.

I told the Tots firmly, 'No more animals in class.' I even outlawed insects in matchboxes so that there would be no charge of discrimination. For weeks we had quiet lessons in which no cats popped out of desks, no dogs had to be taken out on urgent exercise and nobody's hamster ate the blotting paper. The Carnival of the Animals was over. Yet I didn't feel that I had scored a victory. In fact, I hadn't. With the Tots I never did. They soon had their animals back in class, and without even trying.

It was no less a person than the Headmaster who next introduced livestock to us. He brought them in a box and handed it to me.

'Look after these while Miss Ritchie is away, will you?' he asked.

In the box were two white mice. Miss Ritchie, Biology mistress, kept them for some reason best known to herself. The Tots muttered darkly about vivisection or 'Cutting Things Up,' but I knew that this wasn't true of the mice. They were part of one of Miss Ritchie's teaching schemes. I didn't know exactly which principles they were intended to illustrate, but I found that out eventually.

Titch and Basher, who had had experience of mice-keeping, they said, volunteered to clean out the box daily and feed the mice. I was glad to have nothing more to do with them than taking an occcasional peep into the box to see that they were alive and well. We came back one Monday morning to find them extremely well.

'W-a-a-ah, Miss,' said Dinny, peering into the box. 'There's six mice now. Where did the new ones come from?'

Mavis supplied Dinny with background information on this topic. Soon the class was buzzing with the facts of the two mice making six.

The Tots were delighted with the new mice and Basher knocked up a large box to house the family. All the Tots said they would be sorry when Miss Ritchie returned and took the mice back. Only I hoped that Miss Ritchie would return, and soon! I asked around the staff and there seemed to be no one who could help me distinguish a male mouse from a female.

When the next lot of baby mice arrived Basher declared that they were overcrowded and needed exercise. Each morning he let the mice out of the box and they ran up the water pipes and along the window ledges. Then Basher collected them and put them back into their box.

One morning Basher said we were one mouse short. Another class was due to come into our classroom and still the mouse could not be found.

'I won't come into a room in which a mouse is running amuck,' said the mistress of the class waiting outside. So the Tots and I ransacked the cupboards, desks and every place which might hide a white mouse. There was a movement behind the book cupboard.

'There it is,' yelled Titch. The mouse, scared out of its tiny wits, streaked through the open classroom door and across the playground, followed by Titch. The constant wearing of plimsolls gave Titch a flying start in all impromptu sprints. I grabbed a hockey stick and followed Titch and the mouse.

'Don't kill it, Miss,' said Titch.

'I'm not going to kill it. I want to block its path so that you can catch it.'

The mouse couldn't have been reassured about my good intentions because it took one look at me and scuttled into Mr Gideon's classroom. Titch and I followed and soon Mr Gideon's classroom was in a finer uproar than usual. Titch, Giddy and I crawled on our hands and knees beneath the desks. The Tots had now left their own classroom and all forty of them were outside the door of Mr Gideon's classroom shouting encouragement.

'The mouse is in the waste-paper basket, Sir.'

'Nah. You missed him. He's in the chalk box, Miss.'

The Tots, as commentators with an overall view of the pitch, were excellent, disregarding the fact that they reported where the mouse had been instead of where it was. When it was in Square Four we were told that it had last been seen in Square Three.

At last the mouse lost patience and, dashing between the children's feet, made for the open playground. Mr Gideon grabbed a hockey stick and ran out after it, shouting 'Don't worry. I'll kill it for you.'

'No. No. We don't want it killed,' I yelled. 'It's Miss

Ritchie's. We only want it caught.' But Giddy did not appear to have heard.

Titch hared after Giddy, waving his hand above his head and jumping up and down, an antic which he regarded as proper before addressing a teacher. 'Don't kill him, Sir,' pleaded Titch. 'He's One of Ours.'

Still clutching my hockey stick, I followed several panting paces behind Titch. By this time Giddy had cornered the mouse and seemed to be going in for the kill. The Tots on the touchline were jumping up and down and shouting entreaties to spare the life of their pet. But, in the pandemonium, Mr Gideon couldn't hear a word. I was the only person with a weapon so I was forced to use it.

I nipped in front of Giddy and tackled him. The hockey sticks met with a crack. As they did so the Headmaster appeared round one corner and the mouse disappeared round another. The way it looked to Mr Norris, two teachers had left their classes, screaming like pop fans, and had indulged in a game of hockey with an imaginary ball.

At the sight of the Headmaster, Mr Gideon's class disappeared like ferrets down a hole and my lot lined up smartly. Only Giddy and I were snapped in a bad light, dishevelled and gasping.

'Mr Gideon was helping me to chase a mouse,' I explained.

Mr Norris looked at us and said nothing. That was a bad sign. His silence was, in itself, a censure.

Giddy and I slunk back to our classes and the Tots spent the rest of the day conjecturing on the likely fate of the white mouse. Dinny said he would probably go and live with the field mice. This thought comforted the Tots, so I did not argue.

I was glad when Miss Ritchie returned and took the mice off our hands. Miss Ritchie was a sensible, solid girl with large hands and small wonder. Nothing ever surprised her, not even the gas man in the ladies' cloakroom. She was a thoroughly suitable girl to have the custody of mice because, apart from her talents as a teacher of Biology, she played a very useful game of hockey.

VII

There was an unexpected advantage gained when teaching Music at Sunnyfield. I never went short of fresh vegetables.

The Music room overlooked the gardens where Mr Avery tried to instil into the Tots and the Big Uns the rudiments of agriculture.

From the window of the Music room I couldn't help seeing what went on, and what didn't go on, in the way of work while Mr Avery's back was turned.

The gardening boys knew that, in the Music room observatory, I was in a position to make trouble for them if I wished. They overcame this danger by friendliness and unabashed bribery.

I was thumping through 'Nymphs and Shepherds' on the piano, with the choir hot on my trail and only half a bar behind when Titch's face leered up at me through the slot in the open window.

'Psst! Miss!'

The class was in full throttle on the 'Sacred to Ee-ee-ee-ee —ease' bit.

'What is it?' I hissed back at Titch.

'Miss. Do you like carrits an' unyons?'

I was knocked back a bar or two by the question, but I

recovered and said I supposed I *did* like carrots and onions. 'Right-o,' said Titch. 'We planted some carrit and unyon seeds this morning and if they come up I'll give yah some. Tha's a promise.' He jerked a dirty thumb to confirm the bargain and returned to leaning on his spade.

The other boys who had gardening implements sturdy enough were also leaning on them. The underprivileged with frail tools or none were standing around reading comics and bracing themselves for the moment when Georgie, the duty 'look-out' signalled that Old Digger was again coming into orbit. Then all fell to work, stopping only to wipe imaginary sweat from their faces or to ask for a drink of water.

Spring was sudden that year. From the Music room we could smell the lush perfume of growth. The gardening boys took off their jackets and hung them on earth-rooted spades. This made the spades even more comfortable for leaning on. From the Music room I heard the song of the birds and the regular farming reports from the boys outside the window.

'They've come up, Miss, them carrits an' unyons.'

Titch, shirtsleeves rolled up against the remote possibility of work, peered up through the open window. At the time I was trying to get a few spiritually tone-deaf characters to take a Mozart gem on one week's free trial. I wasn't feeling like discussing crops. Titch took my silence for disbelief. A black-nailed hand was thrust through the window at me. The hand clutched a bunch of 'carrits an' unyons' about the thickness of cotton threads.

The class, who couldn't see the rest of Titch, were

astonished but glad of any respite.

'Go away,' I said. 'I'm busy.'

'But these is yourn, Miss, these is.'

'What is the point of pulling them up, at that size?' I said, ungratefully.

'I'm not picking 'em,' said Titch. 'I just takes 'em out every so often to see how they are gettin' on, then I puts 'em back.' And Titch stumped back to his plot and did just that.

If Titch's gardening was unorthodox, Basher also had his surprising agricultural moments. One morning he scuffed into class, slung on his desk a satchel bulging with old comics and announced, 'They started a School Pet Club yesterday, Miss, and I joined.'

'Oh, I see. What's your pet?'

'Farmer Snelling, he give me two piglets,' Basher went on. 'I'm going to feed them. When the pigs is big enough to go for bacon I'll sell 'em for 'undreds of pounds.'

'Cruel,' said Dinny.

'Yah! Two pigs are not worth that much money,' said know-all Titch.

'They will be if *I* feeds 'em,' Basher pushed out his green woollen sweater on his pig-breeder's chest.

Basher was allowed to do some pig-tending during gardening lessons. The pigs were housed in a sty on an allotment adjoining the school. So now, in addition to Titch's crop reports, I also received Basher's livestock news through the open window.

After several weeks of hard work I had managed to teach a class a song with a slippery sort of descant. The notes died away as Basher's head and shoulders appeared in the window. He looked like a Punch and Judy puppet.

'They're doin' lovely, Miss,' he said and jerked me a grubby 'thumbs up' sign.

'Glad you think so, Basher.' I had never guessed that Basher had musical leanings.

'I reckon they're good enough to take a prize,' he went on.

'Well,' I said, 'I had thought of entering them for the local Eisteddfod.'

Basher had never heard of an Eisteddfod but it was a principle of his never to admit ignorance.

'Very likely, Miss.' He nodded wisely. 'Just a few more weeks on good swill and they might take a prize.'

The clank of Basher's swill buckets continued to flail the spring and summer air. The sound mingled with the crack of cricket and the whack of tennis balls. We heard it floating across the playground when we were tangling with plainsong or soul-deep in Sibelius. Whatever the choice of music, Basher's swill-bucket tympany accompanied it.

After school, while we were waiting for the bus, the Tots and I leaned on the sun-warmed wall of the pig sty and watched Basher's protégées, Curly and Albert. Curly was a noisy pig with a tail like tortured spaghetti. Curly squealed a great deal and nipped around like a Harlem Dodger. Albert was a loutish character with shifty eyes and practically no muscular co-ordination. He stood in the trough and refused to move, even when Basher prodded him with the business end of a window-pole. Albert caused Basher as much trouble by his stolid refusal to budge as Curly did by his over-activity. Watching Basher with the pigs was fascinating. It was surprising that a heavily built, slow-moving boy could be so nimble on his feet.

Before Basher took to pig-tending there was never any necessity for alacrity. He never had to run for the school bus because he had an arrangement with Titch that he should secure a seat for both of them. If Titch failed in this, it was only he who needed to move fast, to escape Basher.

Basher now began to find agility necessary. As he entered the pig-house with the swill bucket Curly and Albert lunged at him. Basher jumped aside, and as the pigs were re-grouping for a second assault, Basher poured the swill into the trough. The pigs grew larger and fleeter and the operation for Basher became more perilous. But Basher said it was all in a good cause. The Pet Club profit would buy a television set for an Old People's Home.

As the spring progressed wallflowers burnished the Headmaster's garden. The 'carrits and unyons' grew and so did the pigs. The whole school relaxed and threw open the doors and windows.

The form of punishment which all children hated was to be made to stand in front of the class. They hated it because it involved the possibility of being discovered by Mr Norris, who collected all wrong-doers and hauled them back to his study, where they were expected to explain their misdemeanours.

In the days when Basher was over-extravagant with the use of his fists he found his way to the Headmaster's study. Basher admitted thumping another boy in class and, when asked why he behaved badly, looked at the floor, grew flashy about the ears and shook his head.

'Dunno, Sir,' he said, 'because I likes English with Miss. She learns yah good.'

Perhaps only Basher could have delivered a compliment and an indictment in the same breath.

Student teachers came to spend some time at Sunnyfield. To my surprise one of them, a zealous young man named Mr Tremlin, was assigned to watching my Music lessons. I thought this unusual. Pinks Thomson had an explanation. He told me of the need to instil in students a sense of caution. My music lessons would be, he said, the best cautionary exercise any young teacher could receive. I would be giving an essential service, a service which very few could provide.

Mr Tremlin was a likeable, pale man who loved music. He tried to like children but found it hard going. He sincerely wanted to understand the Tots and they were very curious about him. There was the best of goodwill on both sides yet they never came to terms.

Mr Tremlin sat for many hours trying to assess the Tots and the Tots sat trying to assess Mr Tremlin. The outcome was that the Tots found it extraordinary that Mr Tremlin had never heard of the Gambols and Mr Tremlin found it extraordinary that the Tots had never heard of minor madrigal composers.

One morning he offered to amend their ignorance on Elizabethan music and went into his spiel. It was delightful to listen to him. Both the classroom doors were open and there was no sound but the lazy hum of the bees and the lazy grumbling of the gardening boys as they moved the hoe from one hand to the other. There was a settled, peaceful air about the school. I could have dropped off to sleep if I had not been fascinated by Mr Tremlin and his singing. Mr Tremlin's music-making was both beautiful and precise. The only thing the Tots didn't find precise was Mr Tremlin's counter-tenor voice. They couldn't decide if it was the voice of a man or a woman.

The Tots looked curiously at Mr Tremlin. They were under the influence of the daily newspapers and had heard of sex-changes. I was relieved when their minds were distracted.

A huge lorry rumbled to the allotment. The time had come for Basher's pigs to go to the bacon factory. Basher went off to supervise their departure. The Tots were fond of Curly and Albert and a sort of gloom descended on the class. It wasn't helped by Mr Tremlin's bi-sexual rendering of a song which invited death. But Mr Tremlin was a kindly man and not insensitive to the Tots' feelings about the pigs.

'I'll try to keep their minds on other things,' he whispered to me as he soared off on another song. I wished he might never know what other things.

'My lady fair,' sang Mr Tremlin.

Basher appeared at the window. He looked very worried.

'Curly don't want to go,' he said. 'He's chasing about and squealin' something horrible.'

I told Basher to be quiet and indicated that he should get on with his brutish work and leave us to soak in musical culture. Luckily Mr Tremlin hardly noticed the interruption. He didn't even notice when, on one of his dying-fall notes, a pig shot through the classroom like a fast ball from a fresh bowler.

The pig was followed by the two bacon men, in overalls and peaked caps. As the men dashed through they just had time to touch their caps deferentially to Mr Tremlin.

As the men's heels disappeared through one door Curly, on his second circuit, appeared at the other door. Quickly on Curly's tail followed the men and on their tail followed Curly, on his third time around. It was like repeatedly watching the same sequence of an old film.

The last time around the pig went under the piano. Mr Tremlin, who was as nifty about the feet as an electric organist, trapped the pig between his feet and held it.

When all was over Basher returned to the classroom to collect his football boots and his thoughts.

'I think I'll jag in this pig-breedin' lark, Miss.' Basher hung the football boots around his neck. His dejected face between the boots bore the expression of one mentally in the stocks.

'Don't say that, Basher.'

'Nah, Miss. I reckon I'll take up a diffrint hobby. I reckon I'll playa piana.'

Basher sat at the piano and put a determined foot on each pedal and both hands behind his back.

'Placc your hands on the keys, Basher.'

'Nah, Miss.' Basher shook his head and the boots joggled vehemently. 'I shan't bother with no keys. Just playa pedals, like Mr Tremlin. I reckon he's very handy with his feet.'

I told Mr Tremlin of Basher's sudden interest in music and before Basher's resolution had time to cool Mr Tremlin was giving Basher piano lessons in the lunch-hour.

I was afraid it wouldn't last; that sooner rather than later Basher, Mr Tremlin or the piano would weaken. I never did discover which threw in the towel first but all three looked the better for the termination of the experiment.

About the whole business Mr Tremlin would commit himself only so far as to remark that Basher's talents wouldn't run to waste in an area in which grape-plodding was an earnest and respected pursuit.

VIII

When apple blossom frothed on the tree beside the school pigsty, love came to Basher. It flew from the East and it arrived unexpectedly in the classroom in the company of the Headmaster.

'This is Maya,' he said. 'She has come from Hong Kong and she will be with you for a few weeks. I want you to make her feel at home.'

The Tots turned their stunned gaze on a deliciously attractive little person of about their own age in a white and gold embroidered dress. Her dark hair fell on her shoulders and eyes the colour of violets peeped out enchantingly from long black lashes. Maya was a real 'turn up' for any book.

'Good morning,' she said and lifted an exquisite small hand to shake mine. Her golden charm bracelet tinkled as she moved and when she smiled her even teeth were startlingly white against the golden tan of her skin.

'Wa-a-a-ah! Whe-e-e!' said the Tots. I could hardly blame them for letting slip the odd unguarded ejaculation. I was making a mental one or two myself. Maya seemed like an exotic creature from another world, a world of pomegranates and peacocks – a Scheherezade come to Sunnyfield.

Mr Norris explained to me that Maya's father was in the Army and that the family was staying in the district for a short time before going abroad again. I gave Maya a desk beside Sandra, a Tot whom I considered the nearest I could come to a suitable companion for the poised and elegant Maya. The Tots nearly fell out of their seats in their eagerness to provide Maya with the tools of their trade: pencils, exercise books, text-books, etc.

Both the boys and the girls regarded Maya as A Personage. She was someone whom they could flaunt to the rest of the school as a sort of Tots' status symbol.

'Have you met my friend Maya from up over Hong Kong?'

The Tots' interest in Maya was excessive and quite uninhibited. Mavis leaned forward and shouted to me in a loud, delighted whisper.

'Miss. She got butterflies on her shoes.'

All eyes turned to Maya's dainty feet. It was true. On the front of each shoe was a butterfly made of coloured beads.

I did not realise that love had hit Basher until I saw him combing his hair in class. It was a thing he rarely did, as far as I could see, in class or anywhere else. Now he had somehow become possessed of a large, violent-green comb which he wielded on every occasion, suitable or unsuitable.

At first I could hardly believe that Basher was interested in a girl. He had treated the girl Tots with nothing but friendly tolerance and an odd prod in the back when they sneaked on him reading comics in class. But I was certain that Basher was 'taken' with Maya-worship when he started to show off in class. He had always done this, within the bounds of prudence. It was part of Basher's role as leader of the Tots that he should go as far as he dared with 'Miss.' In his effort to draw attention to himself now, he went too far.

'He's going through a phase,' said Pinks Thomson when we were discussing Basher in the staff-room. 'Most boys go through it when they first realise that girls are anything more than just a nuisance. Let Basher see you won't stand for impertinence.'

'I have given him punishments,' I said. 'I've talked to him. I've tried everything.'

'Try shaking him,' said Pinks.

'What?'

'Shake him – in front of the rest of the class. Doesn't hurt the boy. Only hurts his vanity. Does the world of good.'

'Does it?'

'Yes. You try it.'

I suppose I would not have thought any more of Pinks's advice if I hadn't caught a cold and lost my voice, temporarily. It made teaching forty children very difficult and Basher wasn't any help. I had to write everything I wanted to say on the blackboard and while my back was turned Basher got up to his tricks.

From the titters going around the class I gathered that he was doing a pretty good imitation of 'Miss' croaking her instructions. He sounded like a demented seal and, turning quickly to catch him at it, I saw that he also looked like one. I almost wanted to laugh. I opened my mouth to reprimand Basher but no sound came.

At this Basher gave another seal-like bark, flapped his flippers, and the whole class collapsed in helpless laughter. I could see that, if I was ever to teach the Tots, some sort of effort had to be made to bring Basher into line. I walked to Basher's desk and indicated that he should stand up. I put on my 'stern teacher' face. There was tense silence in the room.

My first shock was that Basher seemed to have grown in the last few weeks. He was now almost as tall as I was. He had his jacket off and I was confronted with an expanse of green pullover.

Pinks had not given me blow-by-blow instructions for Schoolboys, the Shaking Of. I didn't know how to begin. I found I didn't even *want* to begin. But I knew that on my next move depended class discipline for many months.

I reached out a hand and grabbed at Basher. All I seemed to have dredged up was a handful of green pullover. I yanked the jersey towards me but Basher remained as immovable as if his feet were set in concrete. His only re-action seemed to be a stare of mild admiration at the stretch of his pullover. I think Basher's mother had bought one of green elastic.

The Tots were just as bewildered as Basher by my sudden and eccentric behaviour. The bell for the end of lesson rang and I released the pullover cautiously. I didn't want the kick-back to do Basher any injury. I left Basher staring at the small hump of green wool in the middle of his chest and musing on the unreliability of women teachers and boughten wool.

Maya saved the situatiom. She came to my desk, where I

62

sat feeling more shaken than Basher would ever be.

'Would you care for one of my sweets, Miss?' she asked. 'It may perhaps ease your sore throat.'

I croaked my thanks and took a boiled sweet. The Tots continued collecting their books and giving more than a general ear to the conversation. Maya looked at the Tots and shook her pretty head.

'I do not know how you tolerate their rudeness,' she said. 'In my last school it was considered ill-mannered to be rude to one's teacher. At my school there were no boys. Boys are uncouth.' She flashed a very significant glance in the direction of Basher. I saw his ears redden and guessed that, with the word 'uncouth' Maya had shaken Basher more successfully than I could ever do. And so she had.

Basher became his old self, I regained my voice and lessons were once more pleasant. Maya's continued presence stimulated the Tots to strange discoveries.

'Maya's Mum got servants up over Hong Kong,' Mavis confided to me. 'She's got no washing machine but she got a lady instead, and Maya's Mum got a black dress with no back in it! She wears it to cocktail parties.'

'Wassat?' asked Sweet William. Filling the gaps in Sweet William's knowledge was like filling a bath with a trickling tap and the bung out.

'Cocktails is drinks,' said Basher, wishing to prove himself a man-of-the-world in Maya's eyes. 'They had cocktails on the telly.'

'With little cherries on sticks,' added Mavis. 'And people stands up and talks at cocktail parties and they don't never sit down. Not never!'

63

The vision of people with no backs in their clothes standing about holding cherries on sticks confused Sweet William. He looked slowly from Mavis to Basher. Sweet William's great bovine eyes looked like dark pools in which comprehension was about to go down for the third time.

'Don't they have nothin' to eat?' he asked. 'No jelly or ice-cream.'

'Course not,' said Mavis. 'They eats little biscuits with bits of meat and fish and stuff on them. I helped my Auntie make some cocktail snacks. They was lovely.'

'I likes jelly and ice-cream,' mumbled Sweet William, no member of the gastronomic *avant-garde*.

Not long after this discussion the subject of parties arose again. Miss Girlan, the Domestic Science mistress, a pretty dark-haired girl able to make vol-au-vents rise to her bidding, told the Tots that they might prepare a party menu. Inspired by Maya's Mum, the Tots requested a cocktail party. Miss Girlan agreed and we were all invited to the 'cocktail party' one lunch break.

The 'cocktails' were mostly 'fizz' and squash but as each drink contained a cherry on a stick the Tots considered that technically it was a cocktail party.

Some of the boys were dubious about a party so sophisticated as to exclude jelly. Very cautiously they entered the Domestic Science room where the girls, wearing frilly aprons, handed around trays of *canapés*, potato crisps and 'cocktails.'

One look at the food convinced the boys that the party was, after all, worthy of their attention. The girls passed among their guests with laden trays and returned to base

64

clutching the empty trays as if fearful that they also might be snatched.

Basher stood around trying to engage Maya's attention by looking like his version of a TV hero.

'Scotch onna rocks anna twist of lemon.'

'Here's a orange squash and don't spill it,' said Mavis.

I can't claim that the conversation at that cocktail party was any better or any worse than at most cocktail parties, but there was less of it. There was hardly any conversation except that about the food, and that only when the Tots could spare time from eating.

Maya, in a silk dress the colour of wild orchids, behaved most elegantly and handled her disposal of a cherry stick as one accustomed to the disposal of social flotsam and jetsam. Toddy put his cherry-stick behind his pencil-less ear, thus making his stance for the afternoon a little more level and less non-conformist. Junky used his stick for picking his teeth and Titch pinned his cherry-stick proudly in the lapel of his jacket, among the pins and badges and the king-size paper clip which he hoped one day might 'come in handy.'

The cocktail party was a success. Even the most case-hardened jelly-eaters agreed about that. Standing up to eat had advantages the Tots had not suspected. There was no need to sit patiently hoping that you would get a second helping. A circulating eater could himself ensure that his plate was never empty. The Tots declared that there was, in their opinion, a big future in this mobile eating.

By this time Basher had got around to performing little deeds of devotion, such as sharpening pencils for Maya and keeping her a seat on the school bus. His behaviour in class became so good that I feared I might have to describe it as 'exemplary.' I guessed that Maya also influenced Basher's sudden interest in joining the R.A.F. and going 'Abroad,' since 'Abroad' was where Maya would soon be.

'I shall be a pilot,' Basher told me, decisively.

'You will have to work hard at school. You need a good educational background.'

Basher gave me a look which indicated that he considered me exactly the sort of person to put the realistic 'mockers' on a man's ambition and love-life.

Having made the decision that he would, at some future date, bestow himself upon the R.A.F., it was now up to Basher to communicate this to Maya. He wanted her to know that the humble schoolboy and part-time pig-keeper she now saw before her was not the dashing Basher of the future. He managed to convey this information, very neatly I thought, during an English lesson.

The Tots were giving one-minute speeches on 'What I Want to Be When I Leave School.' It was a hackneyed subject, but one on which every Tot had something to say, even Sweet William.

'Dunno,' he said. It was, I suppose, better than nothing.

Basher could hardly wait to be asked to speak. At last he scraped back his chair and stood up.

'When I leave school I am going to be a pilot in the R.A.F. It will be very difficult to get in the R.A.F. because they do not have just anybody. You have got to be clever and you got to pass examinations, which I shall do.'

'Wa-a-a-ah!' said Mavis. She had never before heard

Basher or any other Tot offer, in cold blood, to take examinations.

'And when I am a pilot,' Basher continued, 'I shall be flying mostly abroad. I shall be up over abroad most of the time. I shall come home to see our Mum and our Lionel and most likely I will take them up over abroad, too, because the sunshine abroad will be good for my Mum's bad leg.'

With this combination of space-man and medical missionary Basher could hardly lose. The Tots were impressed. They applauded Basher and his ears glowed like two traffic indicators.

'Now Maya will tell us what she wants to be when she leaves school,' I said.

Maya stood up and folded her delicate hands before her.

'When I leave school I intend to take up a career in nursing,' she said. 'It is a thing which I have long wanted to do because a nurse is a good and useful person in the community. Also her uniform is very nice and she may marry a doctor.'

This information threw Basher for a moment but he seemed satisfied that a pilot could give a doctor good competition, any day.

'To train as a nurse I want to come to London,' said Maya.

Basher's jaw fell. He realised the truth. While he was planning to go abroad, Maya was planning to come to England. If he became a pilot, their paths might never cross unless he was in an accident and he didn't fancy that. When class was over Basher sauntered over to my desk.

'When I am a pilot, do I have to go up over abroad, Miss?'

'You will probably have to go where you are required, Basher.'

Basher considered for a moment, then he made a valiant decision. Renouncing his all at the call of duty, Basher did the far better thing.

'Oh, well,' he said, 'I suppose you got to go where your country needs you.'

Slinging his satchel of comics over his shoulder, Basher strode, mentally, into the sunset.

IX

The Tots' most endearing quality was their tolerance of human weakness in general, and of mine in particular. They not only tolerated my weakness of often being late for school. They also abetted it.

When the first school bell rang the Tots lined up outside the classroom or, if it was wet, went inside. I was supposed to be there to call the register and lead them into Assembly in the Hall. But, when it was obvious to the Tots that I wasn't going to arrive in time to do this, Mavis did the honours. By the time I got off the late bus the Tots would be streaming back from Assembly.

'Headmaster was asking for you,' Mavis said. 'I told him you were here.'

'It was well-meaning of you, Mavis, but you musn't tell lies,' I said.

'It's not lies because you *are* here, aren't you?' Mavis could have talked Joan of Arc off the stake.

'I know just how 'tis, Miss,' said Junky one morning when he and I, the two notorious late-comers of the class, were sitting in the classroom waiting for the Tots to return from their hymn-singing.

'I can't get up in the mornings, either,' said Junky.

He knew that, as a late-comer, he should have been sent to the Headmaster to make an explanation and, if necessary, be punished. Junky also knew that I hadn't the gall to send him. So he settled down to a cosy chat about our common weakness.

'What you wants, Miss, is a little car of your own,' said Junky. 'Then you wouldn't have no bother about missing buses and waiting half an hour for the next one.'

When the rest of the Tots returned they also agreed that a little car would be just the thing for me. I said it would be very nice but I couldn't afford one.

'My Dad'll get you one cheap,' Junky offered. 'Nothin' special, of course, but you won t mind about that, will you, Miss?'

So it was that one day a little 'nothin' special' on four wobbly wheels arrived in the school playground. It looked like a mini-hearse. The car had a slight list to starboard on account of a broken spring and when I started the engine the tappets played a banjo solo. The car's registration letters were EPA, so we named her 'Eapa Junk' or mostly just 'Eapa,' and the Tots and I loved her.

The first day I drove to school and arrived before the first bell rang, the Tots, standing around in the playground, cheered as though they were welcoming the winner of the Le Mans motor race.

As I switched off the ignition and the old car shuddered to a standstill the Tots gathered round her and popped their heads in at the open windows. I usually drove Eapa

70

with the windows down, for the very good reason that they wouldn't wind up. On a very wet day I had to wear a sou'wester hat.

'Did you change the oil like I told you?' asked Sweet William.

'You needs a new pair of boots,' Basher interrupted. I agreed that my shoes were getting old.

'Nah, Miss,' said Basher. 'The car needs new boots – new tyres.' Basher stubbed his right foot against one of the pretty bald tyres.

'Do she start up all right from cold, Miss?' Titch enquired. 'She'll get cold standing in the open all day. What Eapa wants is a muff for the radiator.'

'I'll knit one,' Dinny volunteered. 'I knitted my Auntie a lovely tea-cosy.'

'D-a-a-aft!' Titch sneered.

That morning the Tots and I went into Assembly together. I don't know if the Headmaster noticed this, but he did give a little talk on faith rewarded.

The Tots took Eapa Junk to their hearts, as they did any stray dog which wandered into school. Perhaps they liked Eapa because she was old, unshiny and eccentric. The Tots cared little for perfection in anything. They preferred something which invoked sympathy.

Sweet William made a name for himself as the class authority on motor engines; a heady situation for a boy who had never before been an authority on as much as the day of the week. The mechanical information came from Sweet William's big brother. He supplied it, Sweet William misunderstood it and I misapplied it.

71

One evening as the Tots sat in the school bus waiting to go home they watched as I tried to start Eapa. The old car whirred, coughed and shook but she wouldn't start. The Tots hung out of the windows of the bus shouting.

'Give her a bit more choke, Miss.'

'Nah. Try her *without* the choke.'

Suddenly the Tots could endure non-participation no longer. They clattered down the steps of the bus and rushed to the aid of Eapa.

The bus driver, who was about to climb into his cab, looked astonished to see his cargo off-loading itself. He raised his eyes in a devout prayer for patience and came over and joined the crowd.

'Get inside, Miss,' he said. 'Take off the brake and we'll give her a push. When I give a shout shove her in gear.'

The Tots and the driver pushed and the little car lunged forward and made straight for the pigsty. To avert disaster I stamped hard on the brake, leaving the Tots and the driver grunting and heaving.

'Now, Miss,' said the bus driver, coming round to the driver's window to give me an old-fashioned look, 'take that brake off and do try to co-operate.'

The next time Eapa moved I steered away from the pigs. We circled the small playground once, twice, three times but Eapa would not start. Home-going children and staff collected to cheer, jeer and give advice. The bus driver examined the plugs and declared he could find no reason for Eapa's stubbornness.

It was strange that it took Mr Norris, an academic-type Headmaster, not much addicted to the mechanical, to spot the flaw. As Eapa rumbled by his open study window on her next turn around the track, he leaned out.

'Have you switched on the ignition?'

I have never known a man so swift to detect essentials.

Eapa chugged into life and a cheer went up from the spectators. The driver took off his cap, scratched his head and said he couldn't understand for the life of him why the car wouldn't start before. Either he had not heard the Headmaster's remarks or he had gone to school in the days when teachers were considered infallible.

The Tots' experience of teachers was otherwise. They gave me reproachful looks and piled on to the bus again.

It was about the time we had Eapa that Titch became so engrossed in work that he began missing the school bus and cadging a lift home in the evenings. One evening as I drove along the rain-lashed road I saw his figure trudging along.

I stopped and Titch climbed into the front passenger seat. He put his plimsolled feet comfortably on the dashboard and, above the slap of the tappets, told me his story.

'I was tidying up the Games Cupboard for Mr Critchley,' Titch said, 'and when I had finished the school bus had gone so I had to walk.'

I took Titch home and dropped him at the gate. He hopped out and gave a friendly wave as Eapa set off again through the rain. In the driving-mirror I saw that Titch did not open the gate of his house but instead walked away in the opposite direction.

He did the same thing the next evening and each subsequent evening when pressure of school business made him

73

miss the bus. I didn't mind going a little way out of my direction to see Titch safely home, but he never seemed satisfied when he got there. He turned around and walked back in the direction from which we had come.

One evening Titch was not fast enough in making a get-away. Neither was I. As I stopped the car Titch's mother, a dark, energetic little woman sprinted down the garden path, caught Titch firmly by the collar, and told him to 'Get in the house and I'll deal with you.'

Then, surprisingly, she turned her attack on me.

'I should be pleased if you wouldn't give him a lift home in future,' she said.

I said I was only trying to help. Titch's mother looked at me pityingly.

'The only person you are helping is the man who keeps the sweet shop around the corner,' she said. 'The boy begs a lift from you then spends his bus money on sweets.'

After this incident I ceased to have Titch's company on my drive home. Titch maintained a discreet silence and I thought that the sweet-money racket was over until a conversation I had with Pinks. Pinks was in the staff room looking through some patterns for a new sports coat. He had just reached the most ebullient part of the book and was in a particularly good humour.

'Nice boy, Basher,' said Pinks. 'Often give him a lift home in my car when he has to stay late. He lives my way but I'd never seen him thumbing a lift until recently.'

'*Very* recently?' I asked.

'Mm,' said Pinks. 'Generous boy. Always has sweets. Insists that I take one. Friendly boy.'

74

'Very friendly,' I said, 'friendly with a boy named Titch.'

'I know Titch,' Pinks interrupted. 'Little chap, bright, full of ideas.'

'Jumping with them,' I agreed.

X

From the Tots' classroom it was possible to see the School Games Field. So the Tots kept all games under nosey surveillance for infringements of the rules. In my turn, I had to make a stand for a mite more respect for the educational Queensberry rules.

'Pay attention and don't look out of the window.'

'But it was a foul, Miss. I *seen* it!'

'Mind your own business. Get on with your work.'

This type of daily dialogue grew monotonous so I moved the Sports Commentators to seats where they could not see the field of play. I thought I had the problem, if not beaten, at least partially stunned. But the Tots' interest in the Games Field was immediately resuscitated by First Aid.

'The Headmaster asked me to leave the First Aid box in your classroom,' said Mr Critchley. Standing in the doorway in track-suit, football boots and with wind-whipped fair hair, he looked like a Viking with shortcomings. He parked a large wooden box on the lowest shelf of the Library cupboard. I saw the red cross on the lid and felt gently sick. I have a great admiration for people of the medical and nursing professions. I belong to the breed which feels fragile when it cuts its finger on a salmon can.

'Most accidents happen on the Games Field,' bragged the Sports Master. I had noticed that the members of staff whose business was health-promotion saw more blood-letting in the course of their work than the rest of us put together. 'It will be more convenient to bring the casualties in here,' he said.

At the word 'casualties' I slumped in a chair, visualising a line of stretchers and wan upturned faces beseeching my help.

'Who will . . . er . . .?' (The word 'operate' came into my mind.)

'Don't worry. I'll attend to the casualties.'

No one has felt so relieved, not since Mafeking. Mr Critchley had training in First Aid so all I would be required to do would be to stand about and make comforting noises. I stood up and squandered a smile.

'Of course,' Mr Critchley continued, 'if it's only a case of a minor cut or bruise, you can see to that, can't you?'

I sat down, buckled to the mainspring of my confidence.

The Tots were proud of the First Aid box and eagerly awaited the arrival of our first patient. He arrived before I had had time to mug up the First Aid Manual. He was named George, he wasn't on a stretcher and he looked quite cheerful.

'Fell over. Cut me knee,' he announced importantly. George's claim to fame in the school rested on his owning a sweater embroidered with a wind-jammer and once having had his head stuck in the school railings. His knees had, so far, remained unexceptional.

I sat George on a chair in front of the class and gingerly removed the handkerchief he had tied round his leg. The cut in the knee wasn't deep but the Tots and George were impressed.

'Sbleedin', George,' Titch congratulated him. I looked at the wound, went in to the cupboard, opened the window and took some deep breaths. Then I went back to George. While I cleaned and dressed the cut George gave a blow-by-blow account of how the accident occurred.

'Tha's nuthin',' said Titch. 'I cut me leg once and it bled real bad. There was blood all over the place.'

'Caw!' said the Tots.

'Shall we have another window open?' I asked. 'It seems to be getting very hot in here.'

The Tots leaned forward to get a better view of my bandaging of George's leg. It looked like a pipe lagged in a hurry.

'That bandage is not tight enough, Miss,' said Mavis. 'Shall I do it?'

'Can you?'

'Yes, Miss. I got my Junior First Aid Badge at Club.'

'And me,' said Dinny.

Mavis and Dinny re-bandaged George's knee neatly. The girls' competence inspired in the Tots an interest in the forward march of medical science which could have made it fall back a few steps. The First Aid box became the centre of interest.

'They's lovely splints,' said Mavis. 'Dinny and me does splints.'

'Wassat?' asked Sweet William.

'I had splints when me arm was broke,' bragged Junky.

During the milk-break Mavis and Dinny, with the aid of rulers and scarves, demonstrated how splints were applied. When I returned I feared that disaster had struck. Outside the classroom stood what looked like the morning queue at the Out-Patients' Department. There were stiff-legged 'cripples' with rulers down their socks and all Tots with sizeable handkerchiefs or scarves had at least one arm in a sling. Basher leaned heavily on 'crutches' of hockey sticks and his head was bandaged with a red and white football sock.

'Sick Parade, fall out,' I said sternly, but not too strictly. I didn't want to lose my professional medical staff.

As the weeks passed I realised that when Mr Critchley said he would send me only 'minor casualties' he had meant that I would get a good ninety-nine per cent of his business. A major accident, mercifully, occurred but rarely at Sunnyfield. Yet hardly a day passed without requests for attentions to cuts and bruises and demands for 'sticky plasters.'

Mavis and Dinny were a great assistance but when I was not teaching the Tots I was on my own. Some of the patients sensed this. They entered the room confidently but, seeing no Mavis or Dinny, tried to retreat.

'It don't matter, Miss, if you're busy.'

'Nonsense. You must have your hand attended to. Aren't you the boy I bandaged yesterday?'

'Yes, Miss. I think I'll come back later.'

I can say, quite truthfully, that I never caused pain but I stirred up a considerable flush of despondency. However, under the tutelage of Mavis and Dinny I became less of a medical amateur. But the day came when both Mavis and Dinny failed to come to school, along with about a dozen more of my class.

'Where is everyone today?' I asked.

The Tots who were present looked as if they knew the answer but were disinclined to speak up.

'Are they sick?'

'No, Miss.'

'Perhaps they missed the bus. They may be along later,' I suggested.

'They *won't* be,' said Courteney, decisively.

'Because it's Cobb Hill Fair today,' he said. Courteney had a slightly superior air when he knew something, and even when he didn't. Among the Tots Courteney had a reputation for elegance, which meant that he cleaned the backs of his shoes.

I did know about Cobb Hill Fair. It was a sheep and horse hiring fair which had been held since the beginning of the seventeenth century. Late in the nineteenth century it had been the cause of some stiff letters to the newspapers concerning carters being 'drunk in charge' of their horses. And one horse, Horatio, a bay with a taste for ale, had been found 'drunk in charge' of his driver.

I thought I knew about Cobb Hill Fair but I had overlooked the traditional right (or wrong) of the local schoolchildren to play truant and go to the fair. This right was not recognised by the Headmaster, and he said so, very firmly, to a diminished morning Assembly. The righteous looked very smug and nodded their heads in agreement with Mr Norris. They looked as if it was almost worth missing the fair to be thrust suddenly on such good terms with the Headmaster.

The morning passed quietly until just before noon. I was taking a Music class when one of the Big Uns ran in, looking white and frightened.

'It's Jobbo, Miss,' he gasped. 'There's been an accident. He've fell down the stairs. Come quick.'

It was the situation which I most dreaded. I grabbed the First Aid box and ran across the playground, my heart thudding with fear. Would I be in time? I saw a silent group of boys at the foot of the stairs. The group parted and I saw Jobbo stretched on the floor.

Mercifully, for all concerned, Jobbo was stretched before the competent Mr Critchley.

'Fractured wrist,' said the Games Master. 'Nothing worse, I think.'

The Headmaster arrived and said that Jobbo must go to hospital in town. He suggested that, as I could be 'easily spared,' I should take Jobbo there. Jobbo was made as comfortable as possible and we climbed aboard Eapa. I tried to make cheerful conversation and Jobbo gave me a wan version of his brown-eyed smile and told me not to worry.

'I've been to the hospital before, Miss,' he said. 'I broke my arm twice. Doctor says I got brittle bones.'

At the hospital the receptionist was very pleasant and told us to take a seat. An hour and a half later we were still taking the same seat. Jobbo was patient but I wasn't. I made several trips to reception to point out that Jobbo was still waiting.

'It'll be all right, Miss,' Jobbo said. 'Have a nice cup of tea.'

Jobbo was an authority on the hospital canteen. It seemed that broken and brittle bones were such a common occurrence in Jobbo's family that they had more meals at the canteen than they had at home. As a family they took to plaster of Paris like nuts to their shells.

'You here again?' the nurse said to Jobbo. Jobbo grinned and led the way. He returned, very cheerful, and the nurse said that he had suffered nothing more than the injury to his wrist.

'I'll drive you home now,' I said.

'I'd rather go home on the school bus, Miss.'

'By the time we get back to school the bus will have left.'

There seemed to be some reason why Jobbo wanted to go on the school bus.

'My Mum won't be home,' he said. 'She's gone to my Auntie's today because after school I was going to Cobb Hill Fair. I can't get in if I go home. I was meeting our Norman at the fair. He's got the key.'

The only thing to do seemed to be to go to the fair, find Norman, tell him what had happened and drive both boys home.

Cobb Hill Fair, a few miles out of town, was a happy jumble of fairground and sheep pens. The serious business of the day now being over, the sheep had gone but the fairground was crowded.

I pushed past the man who wanted to guess my weight and the woman who wanted me to buy a doll which 'Walks as it talks and a full set of nylon underclothes.' There was the smell of grass trodden underfoot and of warm candy-floss. Sideshow microphones announced that it was 'definitely the last performance for the time being.' I guessed that 'the time being' would be about ten minutes.

I couldn't find Jobbo's brother Norman. I refused the offer of a 'Rocket Ride to the Moon' and arrived at the 'Roaring Screaming Dodgem Cars.' Roaring and screaming in the cars were Mavis and Dinny, Basher and Titch, Junky and Sweet William and the rest of my missing Tots.

I saw them as they saw me. They wrenched their steering wheels smartly away from my direction but they met with sabotage. The electric current was switched off. It was the end of the ride. We stared at each other foolishly.

I felt as embarrassed as the Tots. I didn't want a platoon of truants delivered into my hands. True it was now out of school hours but the Tots realised that even the dimmest 'Miss' must regard the circumstances as suspicious.

I hadn't come to the fair to find them but it looked that way. It made me seem like a sorry sort of Private Eye. I adopted a preoccupied expression.

'Have you seen Jobbo's brother Norman?' I asked.

The Tots were taken aback at this question. They let Basher handle the conversation.

'Last time I seen him, Norman was by the Hot Dogs.'

'Thank you,' I said.

'Did Norman *do* something, Miss?'

The Tots were curious, but in the circumstances, diffident about asking questions.

'No,' I said. 'It's a long story. You would have known about it . . . if you had been at school today.'

I left the Tots wondering what they had missed, and what they would *not* miss when they arrived at school the following day.

I found Norman and we took Jobbo home. Jobbo looked a little tired but still cheerful. It was not his injury which troubled him but his missing the fair.

'Wish I could have gone to the fair,' he said as Norman put the kettle on for their tea. Their mother had left their tea laid in the kitchen. There were boy-sized chunks of bread and butter, fresh salad and plates of ham and home-made cakes.

'Never mind, Jobbo,' I consoled, 'there's always the fair next year.'

'Mm,' Jobbo mused through a munch of cake, 'it never did me no good going to school today. I should have done what Basher said and . . .'

Jobbo squashed the sentence abruptly. I realised what he was thinking. I admitted to myself that justice did not seem to be batting for Jobbo that day.

The next day there was a great deal of justice. The Headmaster handed it out to all those who had played truant.

'Your lot took the whole affair very coolly,' said Mr Norris. 'They admitted being at Cobb Hill. Can you guess what they said in their defence? They said they thought it must be all right because *you* were there, too.'

XI

Sunnyfield was mostly glass and grass. It was a town school designed for sunshine and activity. Too often we had to get by with rain and sloth.

A spell of wet weather set in. During recreational breaks the school, which usually exploded into the playgrounds and playing fields, was confined to barracks. All who could crammed into the Hall and the rest sat along the pipes in the corridors or among the wet macs in the cloakrooms. Faces were long and tempers short.

Day after day the rain coursed down the windows. The Hall was so crowded that most games were impossible. The children became fractious and the staff desperate. Staff Playground Duty, which now became the task of controlling the mob, was no more a duty but a sentence.

I saw Mr Critchley trying to cope with the seething mass of children in the Hall during the lunch hour. He was trying to organise some activity but the noise was such that even his vocal chords had flagged. He resorted to a blast on a whistle for silence. He stood, panting, perspiration standing on his forehead.

It was a demoralising sight to see such a robust and popular disciplinarian reduced by Hall Duty to nervous rubble. I gave him a look of sympathy and told him that

I couldn't think how he endured it.

He looked at me vengefully. I think he was in a mood when the crumbs of compassion stuck in his throat.

'I am sustained,' he admitted, 'by one thought. It's *your* turn tomorrow.'

I went to sit on the corner of a hard wooden bench-locker in the girls' cloakroom, under the morose cloak of a soggy raincoat. I often sat there to think. It was a place so comfortless that, by comparison, the more flinty tracks of fate seemed less hard.

The weather had entered a phase when rain each day was as inevitable as dawn. I had to decide how, the following day in the Hall, I would keep amused too many children in too little space for too long by half. I turned the problem over and came to the conclusion of Sweet William's favourite cliché, 'Dunno.'

I looked up and saw Mavis and Dinny. They were bursting with an ebullience at odds with my mood and their surroundings.

'Wah, Miss,' said Mavis, fussily pulling aside the wet mac, 'Dinny and me got something to tell you.'

'Has it stopped raining?' It was the only news I wanted to hear.

'No, Miss, but Dinny and me we got an idea. If it rains tomorrow lunch hour, why don't we give a concert, in the Hall?'

'Who?'

'All of us. Our form. We could invite the rest of the school to watch.'

The scheme made enormous assumptions. It assumed talent

on the part of the Tots or tolerance on the part of the audience. There were many arguments against it, and only one for it; I couldn't think of a better idea. The Tots, in full council, gave the idea their unanimous approval.

'Tha's what this school needs,' declared Basher. 'A bitta livening up.'

I hoped that Basher's threatened entertainment (he was stage manager and producer) would be averted but the rain did not let up.

After lunch the following day the school, driven by necessity and curiosity, took shelter in the Hall. The first-comers were given hand-written programmes prepared by the Tots. The supply of programmes soon ran out and the audience would have followed but their retreat was cut off by the incoming crush. The programme-owners showed the programmes to others in the hope that they might raise dissension and a rebel force strong enough to make for out. The programmes did promote some frantic shuffling for the exit but it was too late. Basher closed the doors, gave the signal, and the school was doomed to the opening chorus.

'There's no business like show business,' the Tots' stifled voices informed us from the other side of the stage curtains. Curtain-raising at Sunnyfield was always erratic. Failure on this occasion brought no objections from the audience. A certain muffling of tone was welcome.

Sandra, the accompanist on the audience side of the curtain, thumped extra hard on the piano to penetrate the sound barrier and let the entombed Tots know that help was on the way.

For the audience there was none. The curtain was yanked

up suddenly. Half the performers on the stage had their backs to the audience and were gesturing argument with Basher as to whether they should carry on unseen or stop singing and let Sandra have best.

When they turned and found an audience abruptly laid at their feet most of them were struck dumb. Only Mavis and Dinny and a few other seasoned performers stayed the course. The rest exchanged winks and thumbs up signs with friends in the audience and leers and jeers with enemies.

Sandra came up the straight at a gallop with Mavis and the others not more than three bars behind. They insisted, for the last time, 'There's no business like show business.' The audience, judging on the merits of this free sample, sincerely hoped there wasn't.

Applause was sparse as the singers shuffled off and Titch appeared. He wore his plimsolls, a yellow dressing gown and a fez made of blotting paper hastily stained with red ink. He carried some tennis balls and plastic plates and went into a juggling act. He was accompanied by light music from Sandra and a jabber of heavy interest from the watchers. Unfortunately the interest was not in the juggling, which was adequate in a minor way, but in Titch's hat. The red ink was not dry and the blotting paper soggy. The fez slowly disintegrated and subsided on Titch's head. Down his face ran gory rivulets which disappeared into the neck of his yellow dressing gown. The hat sustained interest for the whole of the performance and Titch went off happily blushing with applause and red ink.

Titch was so inflated with Instant Fame that he was about to reappear for an encore when stage-manager Basher scooped him back into the wings and thrust Junky on to play his harmonica. Junky took fright at the sight of the audience and nervously retreated into the wings, where he received another butt from Basher. This sent him straight to happy semi-obscurity behind the curtains on the opposite side of the stage. There was no way around the back of the stage so Junky now thought he was out of reach of Basher's arm. He was wrong.

Basher plodded on to the stage, grappled Junky into a centre down-stage position, and made an apologetic gesture to the audience.

'Armonica solo by Junky,' he announced.

The harmonica solo re-started. I knew that Junky played only four tunes, 'Drink to Me Only,' 'Home Sweet Home,' 'Now is The Hour' and 'God Save the Queen.' His most popular number with this audience was 'God Save the Queen.' They thought this signalled the end of the concert and a happy release. Some got up to leave.

'Siddown,' directed Basher, flicking his head out of the wings. 'There's more to come.'

Mavis and Dinny were next on the programme. They had taken no risk with their audience rating. They sang a Top of the Pops ballad about a boy who went to his girl-friend's wedding and came over maudlin. Whether he was the groom or not I never did discover. The words were obscured by intensity of vocal emotion and heaving pedal-backing by Sandra. The audience stamped their appreciation.

'Thank you, thank you, everybody' said Mavis in a pseudo American show-biz accent. 'And now me and Dinny will sing the flip side.'

'No you won't, Mave,' came Basher's voice. 'You've had your time so get off and let somebody else have a chance.'

Mavis and Dinny flounced their annoyance and went to sit with their 'fans' in the front row. The school booed and was clearly disgruntled at Basher's Canute-like attitude before the tide of pop music.

The depression sagged even lower at the sight of the next act. On to the stage ambled several lumpish-looking boys in over-long cricket flannels and white shirts. The flannels were hitched at the knees with cycle clips and coloured parcel tape. Some of the boys wore wilted football rosettes. At first sight they appeared to be an away-playing cricket team which had arrived to find itself rained off and forced to pay for a tea of curly sandwiches.

The cricketers suddenly faced the audience and threatened it with raised sticks. This gesture made the front row retreat a floorboard or two. There was a moment of tension and doubt. Then Basher set the record player going. With a sigh of relief the audience realised that it was nothing worse than a display of Morris dancing.

On the small stage at Sunnyfield there were few things worse than dancing. Space was scarce and the structure dodgy. All our theatrical ventures had, of necessity, to be of a sedentary nature. Any untoward movement caused ominous creaking of timber and serious doubts of collapse. The truth is that the stage was not built for dancing, nor were these particular Tots.

The boys had been coerced into learning Morris dancing by Mr Critchley. Given the choice, most Tots preferred pursuits which kept their feet in more constant contact with the ground.

The dancers left the ground infrequently and reluctantly and returned with thudding heel touch-downs. The boys wielded the batons with more abandon than their legs. The exception was Toddy, who was the Fool. It was his task to weave among the dancers and act as a sort of resident comedian. Like all comedy, it was a very serious business. Toddy had to be very agile to avoid the flying batons and serious injury. When the dance ended, leaving the stage and Toddy still upright, I was very thankful. So, I think, was Toddy.

Basher now stood alone on the stage and peered belligerently into the audience. Basher's previous appearances had been concerned with infringements of regulations so everyone looked around to see if anything was amiss. It was. Basher announced that he was about to sing an old music-hall song.

'Wah,' gasped Mavis, turning in her front-row seat to appeal to the audience for Equity standards. 'He's not even on the programme, Sandra hasn't got any music, and what's more he can't sing.'

Mavis's facts were accurate but Basher's reply incontrovertible.

'I'm running this show,' he said, 'I'm the producer.' What he produced was a noise which throbbed on the air like a sore toe. The song was Basher's version of 'Any Old Iron.' If generosity were dredged to rock bottom the best that could be said for it was that Basher knew the words. He knew them but he wasn't going to divulge them. Basher's articulation was so thick and his tone so murky that all traces of the original song were blotted out. The best thing about the act was its speed. Basher seemed to realise that if it were done it were best done quickly, particularly as the exit door was now working like a fly swotter.

Seeing the audience seeping away, Basher finished his song and summoned reinforcements from the Tots. Even Mavis and Dinny signed a momentary truce and jumped on to the stage to join the choir in the final number, 'Bless This House.'

For this the Tots adopted a pious tone and a funereal beat. The inference of religious solemnity threw the escapers off beam. They were conned into the idea that walking out now would be as irreverent as leaving during the National Anthem.

The Tots' finale beat the school bell by a short head and the school thankfully scattered to afternoon classes. At break time I went to the staff-room to collect a cup of tea and, I hoped, compliments on the Tots' initiative. The atmosphere in the staff-room was about as tepid as the tea.

Pinks Thomson was sitting with his suede shoes on the window sill and a watery afternoon sun cooled his turmoiled tweed. He looked around almost churlishly.

'Look here,' he grumbled at me, 'that concert-happy lot of yours, they're trouble shooters. Now, my class, Giddy's class, Miss Tonk's class, everybody's class, they all want to give concerts.'

'Naturally,' I conceded. 'They too want to show off their talent.'

'Talent?' Pinks' eyes hardened. 'Who said anything about talent? What they want, what we all want, is *retaliation*.'

XII

'The Big Uns is having a Mock Election,' Titch informed the class one morning.

'Wassat?' asked Sweet William. Questions advanced to his tongue as readily as answers retreated from it.

'Dunno,' admitted Titch, 'but we ought to have one.'

The Tots felt underprivileged in electioneering so I agreed that they should have their own Mock Election. It seemed a way of imparting a little dusting of knowledge about the Parliamentary system.

'Democracy,' Mavis pronounced. 'That means everybody having a say in the government, don't it, Miss?'

'Yes.'

'Did you have a say in the government, Miss?' Titch propped his elbows on his desk and cupped his hands beneath his chin.

'Well, yes,' I admitted, 'I suppose I did in a way . . .'

'My Dad says the government are a shockin' shower,' countered Mavis in a manner as to the hustings born.

It was difficult to convince the Tots that Mavis's Dad had had a fair crack of the political whip. He had voted, they argued, he had enjoyed full democratic privilege, but he still wasn't getting the government he wanted.

'Democracy,' I explained, 'means having the government which is preferred by the largest number of people in the country.'

'Then Mavis's Dad *doesn't* get a say in the government and a lot of other people do. Tha's not fair, Miss.'

I thought the Tots would better understand if they held the Mock Election. I explained about choosing candidates.

'What they got to do, these candy dates?' asked Titch.

'Make speeches . . .'

'Good. It's talkin'.' Titch was in favour of all pursuits which exercised the tongue and the feet.

'Each candidate must tell us how he will run the country if he is elected.'

The ranks of the Tots were, surprisingly, bulging with people with ideas as to how the country should be run.

'Dustbins ought to be emptied more often,' Titch declared.

'My Gran ought not to have to pay to have her cat seen to,' complained Dinny.

I pointed out that the state of the dustbins and Dinny's Gran's cat were not the direct concern of the Prime Minister. The Tots were perplexed. If the government didn't look after such essential services, the Tots said, what were they doing sitting about 'up over Parliament.'

'It is extremely likely,' said Courteney, 'that my father may take me to Westminster in the holidays.' The Tots turned and regarded Courteney. The introduction of the word 'Westminster' had thrown their comprehension out of gear. No one knew what to say without losing face. No one except Mavis.

'My Dad's taking me to Weston-super-Mare.'

'The Houses of Parliament are at Westminster,' I said.

Titch looked at me with suspicion. 'I thought you told us, Miss, that Parliament was up over London?' He obviously thought I was quite capable of changing the seat of government just to spike the guns of his understanding.

It was decided that there should be three candidates, Courteney, Mavis and Titch. They would each tell the class how they would run the country if they were elected.

Titch was first to jump into the deep end of political oratory. His ideas ran mainly on the bumpy lines of educational reform.

'There should ought to be a swimming pool in every school,' said Titch. 'There shouldn't be no lessons in the afternoons and there should be swimmin' and water-polo. And there should be showers in the changing rooms and the football boots what you lend from school should have *laces*.'

A grunt of approval rose from the boy-Tots. In his reference to laceless boots, Titch had hammered a nail which was considered vital to the political structure. Most of the boys had football boots of their own but forgot to bring them to school when required. Hence the need for the services of the laceless boots.

'And we should not be stuck in classrooms all day,' Titch continued, 'but we should be learned to go on adventure courses and climb mountains and that.'

I had an inspiring picture of Titch, resplendent in laced football boots, surveying the world from the summit of Mount Everest. It seemed possible that, in the years ahead, I might boast of the small part I had played in the formative years of one of the world's smallest men of action. It was a moving thought, that Titch might be the pinnacle success of my teaching life.

'And in my ideal school,' Titch went on, 'there wouldn't be no teachers.' The pinnacle suddenly collapsed.

With this final all-persuasive appeal to right-minded Tots, Titch sat down, amid cheers and desk-thumping. I could hardly see how Courteney could improve on Titch's dream of a schoolboy Nirvana. Yet Courteney's appeal was of a different calibre.

'It is an economic fact,' Courteney began. The Tots looked stunned and speculative about the word 'economic.' 'An economic fact,' Courteney repeated, 'that a large number of people in underdeveloped countries . . .'

Basher was already losing interest. He slid a hand into his desk and reached for a space-comic. Jobbo mooned out of the window and Sweet William stifled a yawn. Courteney was fast losing the attention of his audience. He regained it at a stroke.

'Some people,' he said, 'do not get enough to eat.'

The word 'eat' revitalised the Tots' interest. Basher's comic slid unheeded to the floor. Jobbo left his daydream and Sweet William's jaw dropped another inch, a sign that he was taking an astonished interest in the subject.

'We have plenty of food in this country, like school dinners with cabbage which is very beneficial,' said Courteney. 'The dinners which we do not want could be sent abroad to starving people. That cabbage would do them good.'

'Yeah. Tha's right,' interrupted a generous Junky. 'Fish

pie. They can have my fish pie.'

'Can't send abroad boxes of fish pie,' scoffed Mavis. 'It would go bad!'

Junky scowled at Mavis. He had visualised himself standing on the dockside waving farewell to huge consignments of fish pie. It was a dream which appealed to me also. School fish pie was not particularly repulsive, as fish pies go. It merely happened to be a dish I could well live without.

Although the Tots could not see their way clear to obliging Junky in the matter of fish pie, they did make plans to ship abroad large quantities of cabbage, carrots, rhubarb and prunes.

'If we send all this food abroad, what are we going to eat?' questioned Sandra. She was not less generous but more practical.

'I suggest,' said Courteney, 'that we have simpler school meals. Instead of having different meals each day, we could have ...'

The Tots eagerly hung on his words.

'Fish and chips,' said Courteney.

'W-a-a-a-h!' A gasp of delight went up. Courteney had produced the political bait which no Tot could refuse.

'*Every day*,' emphasised Courteney. Firing the Tots' appetite with this salvo, he sat down. He was clapped and cheered. It was as if the oratory of Titch had never been. I foresaw a landslide for fish and chips and little hope for Mavis, the last speaker.

'If I am elected to go up over Parliament,' Mavis began, 'I shall make a law that kids do not have to stay at school. They can leave, any time.'

The Tots beamed benevolence on Mavis. What was better than any number of school reforms? No school at all.

'Kids could leave school,' she continued, 'they could leave to help their Mums or Dads or get a job and earn good money.'

Here Mavis made her first error in Tot-appeal. The idea of no school was alluring but to thrust work in its place was not a prospect which drew much support.

'What if the kid don't want to leave and go out to work?' Sweet William's dark eyes were apprehensive at the threat of being pushed willy-nilly into the world of wage-packets.

'He can stay on at school if he wants to,' said Mavis.

'I shall stay on at school until I am eighteen,' boasted Sandra.

'C-a-a-w!' breathed Basher. He thought Sandra was taking the cause of individual liberty a bit far.

The ballot papers were handed around. There was much scratching of heads and nibs. Basher collected the papers in an old chalk-box.

I was allowed to count the votes, supervised by the three candidates. The class stood in the aisles or sat on their desks to get a better view of the proceedings. It was soon obvious that Courteney had won the election. The Tots gave a cheer for the winner and for the 'gallant losers.' The vaguer workings of democracy had been demonstrated, or so I thought.

'I voted for Titch,' said Sweet William. 'Why can't Titch be candy date?'

'He was candidate but he didn't get enough votes to be elected.'

'Can't Titch be elected just by the kids who want him?'

'No,' I explained. 'If you happen to vote for the candidate who doesn't win, well . . .'

'You're unlucky. Like my Dad,' said Mavis.

I cannot claim that the lesson improved the Tots' understanding of democracy. It was now regarded as something akin to Bingo and the football pools. You might be lucky or you might not.

However, Titch, the authority on the random vagaries of fate, gave as his opinion that you had a much better chance of hitting the jackpot with democracy than with the pools. This opinion, delivered by a gallant loser, did more than anything to further the cause of democracy among the Tots. They were prepared to try anything as long as they stood a fair chance of winning. Everyone was satisfied, for about a week. Then Sweet William had a complaint.

'Titch,' he grumbled, 'I never see that team on my Dad's football coupon a-Saturday.'

'What team?' asked Titch.

'That team you told us was going to win. Demock or sumthin'. My Dad never heard of it.'

'Democracy isn't a football team,' said the exasperated Titch.

'What is it then?'

'C-a-a-aw!' Titch threw me a harassed glance. I slunk from the room quickly. Every teacher has failures. Democracy, I admit, was one of mine.

XIII

The Tots enjoyed competition, particularly when there was a sturdy possibility of their winning. They liked nothing better than herding their resources to do battle against something or someone, even if it was only 'Miss.'

On occasions the school divided itself into Houses – Yellow, Blue, Green and Red and, in the traditional manner, competed for trophies. The Tots threw themselves into inter-House scraps like lemmings over a cliff. The Tots were in Yellow House. During the periodic bouts of 'House-fever' they wore anything yellow they could lay hands upon. Their conversation, never grandiloquent, was now a tub-thumping assertion of the superiority of Yellow House forces. When I was appointed Mistress of Yellow House they thought it only right that the position had gone to someone 'in the family.'

Each House Mistress coached the girls for Inter-House Sports Day events. The athletic training went on before school, during break, lunch-hour and after school. At all these times the House Mistress had to be present and lit up with enthusiasm. There were times when I doubted that I was equal to the task. The Tots' only doubt was of the suitability of my wardrobe.

'You must wear a yellow dress on Sports Day, Miss,' said Mavis. 'Every House Mistress wears a dress the colour of her House.'

'I don't own a yellow dress,' I argued. Yellow was a colour I avoided. It made me look as if I had just had a nasty shock.

'No yellow dress?' The Tots, who were awaiting the Assembly bell and rummaging in their desks among old toffees, odd plimsolls, comics and marbles, stared at me in disbelief.

'A yellow blouse or skirt would do, Miss.'

I shook my head. I didn't have anything yellow and didn't want to buy anything since I knew I would never wear it out of school. I wanted to avoid the wearing of yellow. Yet, knowing how the Tots doted on it, I knew that if I had turned up one morning with yellow teeth they would have raised a cheer.

Dinny asked couldn't I borrow a yellow dress. I explained that I didn't know anyone with my measurements. The Tots solemnly agreed. They thought it unlikely. Mercifully, the subject was allowed to drop.

During every spare moment from classwork the school was agog with runners running, jumpers jumping, sprinters sprinting and slow-bicycle experts trying not to cycle.

Most of the Tots were prepared for at least one event. Titch arrived at school each morning in running singlet and shorts, having run to school to get in training. It didn't seem to do him any harm, except that he missed the best part of the first lesson in taking off the innumerable sweaters he put on after the run.

Both children and staff were training and coaching for Sports Day. We wore sweaters and shorts for lessons. No one was surprised to see Mr Gideon, in faded shorts, T-shirt and plimsolls, giving a lesson on the effects of the Industrial Revolution. We accepted academic work as a necessary evil between the more important bouts of athletic training.

When we changed classrooms everyone moved according to his chosen sport. Sprinters sprinted, jumpers jumped, hurdlers successfully scaled imaginary hurdles. I timed them with a stop-watch, running with them to make sure that I clicked the watch the very second they touched the winning post. We measured the distances so that they might assess their achievements.

School work assumed an athletic flavour. Essays on 'What I Want to be when I Leave School,' no longer harped on air-hostesses, professional footballers, ballet dancers and pilots. Now everyone wanted to be an Olympic champion.

In the midst of this Mavis made a strange request for my vital statistics, vertical as well as horizontal. She produced a tape measure and I sensed a plot.

'This has nothing to do with my not having a yellow dress for Sports Day, has it?' Mavis admitted that it had.

'You see, Miss,' she said, 'we told the Needlework teacher that you didn't have a yellow dress and she said why didn't we make one for you. She's got a lovely piece of yellow material.'

For a moment I was so overwhelmed that I forgot how nauseated I looked in yellow. The moment Mavis had gone I remembered it. I realised that I could expect a dress, whose style and shade I could not choose and which, from motives of loyalty, I would have to wear to every House function for years, until all the girls who had made it had left the school.

I took Mrs Gegg, the Needlework teacher, aside and asked her to let me see the dress. She was a young, married part-time member of staff. Mrs Gegg doted on peace, decorum and China tea, so she was rarely seen in the staffroom.

She took the dress out of a brown paper bag. I was amazed. It was to a pattern provided by Mavis so it was pretty bobbish in style and the colour I would have described as pale green.

'It's a sort of lime-yellow,' said Mrs Gegg. 'I bought the material for a dress for myself, but later I thought it a little too flashy.'

The dress was the perfect answer to the Sports Day problem. The Tots thought it was yellow and I thought it was green. Both honour and vanity were satisfied.

I felt magnanimous and wanted to repay the Tots, kindness for kindness. Yet there was only one thing they wanted at the time. That was for Yellow House to win on Sports Day. I thought I was in no position to grant this desire. Yet, as it happened, I was.

Sports Day arrived with the sun flashing from a cloud-scudded blue sky. The wind flapped the Union Jack above the Sports Field and rippled the coloured flags which marked the boundaries of the tracks. Everything seemed in movement. The Playing Field seethed with children, parents, friends and teachers.

I wore my new dress and put a yellow bow on Eapa's bonnet. The Tots came festooned with yellow. Basher wore a yellow striped shirt which belonged to (and fitted) his elder brother Lionel and Titch sported yellow and white striped socks. There were yellow shorts, shirts, blouses, dresses, jumpers, ties, bracelets, necklaces and ear-rings. Mavis had varnished her nails yellow.

My name was on the Headmaster's Sports Day duty list as 'Central Controller.' It sounded like a back-room manipulator of subversive rebellion. However, it turned out to be sitting at a table under a chestnut tree, eating ice-cream and keeping a record of the scores. After weeks of strenuous training with the Tots and Big Uns of Yellow House I felt well qualified to sit quietly under a tree. But I didn't feel equally sanguine about being responsible for the mathematical calculations.

At first it was easy. The results from high-jump and long-jump, by the nature of the events, arrived slowly. I had plenty of time to check the additions. But sprinting events brought boys and girls queuing up to have their names and marks entered in the book.

I congratulated each child on his or her success, regardless of House colour. But when Titch arrived among the sprint winners I had to be more circumspect. Even when I restricted my congratulations to other Houses to a smile Titch gave me a look which clearly marked me as a likely Yellow House Quisling. Anyhow, after a while I gave up smiling. The business of adding the scores had become too serious.

As the winners waited and jostled I received couriers from the Headmaster requesting the interim results. I replied and dearly wanted to conclude each note with the phrase 'To the best of my knowledge,' but I was afraid that the paper might fall into the hands of the school governors whom the Headmaster was entertaining.

Old Bill Finch, the reporter on the local weekly paper, joined me at the table. He had come to copy the results in his note-book. Bill Finch was almost as old as his jokes. I should think he was the last remaining working journalist still ploughing through a joke collection culled in the Boer War. The jokes were lengthy and the *dénouements* accompanied by staggering thumps on the table.

Bill was telling me the one about the lady and the bathing machine attendant when he realised that my writing was, for some reason, periodically illegible.

The Tots then came with their parents to make social calls. In other circumstances I enjoyed meeting parents but at the moment I was preoccupied with sums.

Sandra brought her mother to inspect the darts she had sewn in my dress. I had to stand up and give an offhand dress show to prove how well Sandra had darted me. It could have been a pleasant afternoon if I hadn't been haunted by the fact that, the minute the last event was over, the whole gathering would look to me for the final result.

Titch and his mother came to the table.

'Mum won the Mothers' 100 Yards,' Titch boasted.

'Congratulations,' I said. 'Your son is a good sprinter also.'

'He had to learn to be,' said Titch's Mum, 'if he wanted to keep out of the way of the back of my hand. Though I say it as shouldn't, I've always been nippy on my feet.'

I thought how much I could learn from the parents, if only I had the time. Titch peered over my shoulder while I totalled the latest results.

'Green House eighty-four, Yellow House eighty.'

'Green House winning?' Titch looked incredulous. 'Want me to check over your figures, Miss?'

'You may if you wish,' I said, nonchalantly as I could manage. I wanted Titch's mother to think that I was merely humouring the boy. I didn't know what her attitude might be to a teacher who was allergic to figures.

Titch ran his choc-iced finger up and down the page.

'What's this figure here, Miss? In the Yellow House column? Is it a two or a seven?'

'Er, I think it's a two.'

'Nah, Miss. Can't be. Must be a seven. That makes five more for Yellow House. We're winning.'

I didn't like to argue while Titch's mother stood by. The figure did look like a seven and Titch's maths were always accurate. I amended the figure and the total in the Yellow House column.

The results of the last races came in swiftly and as I wrote them down Titch announced the result. According to him Yellow House was still leading by a generous margin. The more Titch checked and added the greater the lead of Yellow House became. The Tots, who had finished competing, crowded around the table under the tree. They congratulated themselves on the result.

The last race ended. The massed crowds, headed by the Headmaster and the school governors, converged on the table. In my panic I couldn't get the figures to agree. However, I didn't worry too much because Titch always got the same answer. Yellow House was the winner, by four points.

'You have checked your figures, of course?' the Head-master asked.

'Titch checked them,' I confessed.

The Headmaster regarded Titch, burgeoned with Yellow House emblems. Mr Norris had been dealing with children for years. He loved them but he didn't expect the impossible.

'Ask Mr Gideon to re-check the figures.'

Mr Gideon did and his results were consistent. The seven in the Yellow House column had, after all, been a two. Green House had beaten Yellow House by one point.

The cups and prizes were presented, speeches made and tea served on the lawn. When it was all over I stayed behind to clear the sports equipment from the field. Titch accompanied me.

'You know, Miss,' he said, picking up a pennant and carrying it before him like a knight entering a tournament, 'we all done our best for the honour of Yellow House.'

I agreed.

'You done your best, too, Miss,' he said, 'that two really did look like a seven.'

XIV

There are few socially acceptable excuses for disliking Shakespeare's plays but the best-loved is that he was ruined by some over-plugging teacher. I resolved never to give the Tots similar grounds for condolence. I would introduce them to Shakespeare, but only at their request. This aim, obviously, would require strategy.

In drama lessons they were working their way through a book of excerpts from well-known plays, one of which was 'A Midsummer Night's Dream.' We were closing our books when Mavis, who always read the backs of books before the front, groaned.

'Oh. Look at the play for next week. It's by Shakespeare. Do we *have* to read it?'

The rest of the class, who seemed to have undergone a course of derogatory brain-washing in the subject, also groaned.

'We will skip the Shakespeare,' I said. 'It's – well – it isn't suitable. You aren't old enough.'

The Tots radared their ears. They were at the 'Finding Out About Life' stage and rooted for anything X-certificate by eleven-year-old standards.

'Why is it unsuitable?' Mavis insisted, flitting her eyelashes until her eyes were expanded rigid with innocence.

'Because—' I tried to look embarrassed and to act Mavis off the stage. 'Because it isn't suitable, that's all. You can read it when you're older.' I left the classroom hastily and heard a rising buzz of curiosity from the Tots.

In the staff-room Pinks Thomson, who had been on Playground Duty, popped in for a hasty cup of tea. He wore a slightly dazed expression, which was surprising since he hadn't had a satisfying laboratory explosion for weeks.

'What's come over your class?' he asked. 'They've taken their play books into the playground and they're reading . . . Shakespeare.'

'Shakespeare? I don't believe it,' said Miss Ritchie, whose faith had been sprained by a sailor and who now preferred everything in writing.

'Remarkable,' congratulated gentle, faded Miss Tonks who spent the best part of her summer holidays living in hope and Stratford-upon-Avon. 'I don't know how you promote such enthusiasm.'

I knew it was going to be difficult to sustain the interest in Shakespeare when they discovered that there was nothing suspect about 'A Midsummer Night's Dream.'

I had one trump card. My class were at an age when they knew there were Forbidden Subjects but were not quite sure what they were. Finding nothing censorable in the play, they began to dredge to find something.

'It's Bottom the Weaver,' Dinny whispered to Mavis under her desk-lid. 'It's, well, it's not nice.'

'Yah. It's not *that*,' scoffed Mavis, the woman of the world. 'I think it's because there's these lovers, see, and they spend the night in the wood. It's wrong to spend the night.'

'My Mum sometimes spends the night at my Auntie Dot's and that's not wrong,' argued Dinny. 'In fact, my Dad says it's a good thing sometimes.'

'That's diffrint,' said Mavis.

'How?'

'Your Mum don't spend the night in a wood.'

The rest of the class shared the feeling that if 'Miss' objected to their reading the play, then they were determined to read it. I had to make some semblance of opposition or the Tots would not enjoy their victory.

'It's Shakespeare,' I argued.

'We wants to read Shakespeare,' the Tots chorused. It would have brought tears to the eyes of Miss Tonks.

Pretending reluctance, I allocated the parts and the play started. From time to time there were sidelong glances to see if 'Miss' would betray anything. All there was to betray was a smug satisfaction at getting Shakespeare off to a good start. The next step, I knew would be more difficult.

One day I asked the Headmaster if the Tots might have an educational outing. He agreed but asked if I really understood what was involved. Forty children in the confines of a classroom were hard work, he pointed out, but at least you knew where they were. Once outside the school forty Tots could be as unmanageable as an escaped flea circus.

When I suggested a day out to the Tots the reaction was more positive.

'W-a-a-ah, Miss. Yes, Miss. When, Miss? How much?'

Not one Tot asked where they would be going. I could sell them into slavery as long as it made a nice day out.

'It will have to be an educational visit,' I warned, 'Where would you like to go?'

'Wembley, Miss.'

'Nah. Tha's not ejoocational. Let's see the crown jools.'

'I seen 'em.'

'An' me.'

'Let's go to the London Sanitarium where you sees the stars and things.'

'How would you like to see a play?' I interrupted.

'Nah. I seen one, Miss,' said Basher.

I cannot claim that the Tots clamoured for Shakespeare on their day out so I tried to find a suitable matinée at a London theatre. There were some excellent plays running but unfortunately they were unsuitable. Not that the plays would give the Tots ideas. They had those already. But I knew that if the Tots quoted some of the play's contents to their parents there might be queues at the Headmaster's door and at the box offices.

So the play chosen was a performance of 'A Midsummer Night's Dream.'

In the early freshness of a July morning the hired coach picked up the Tots. The children were waiting at the bus stops, looking well-dressed, neat and extraordinary.

With his good grey suit Junky wore a flower-splashed shirt and a baseball cap. Basher turned up in a pale blue leather jacket which he had borrowed from his brother Lionel. Lionel had also given Basher a hasty hair-cut. Lionel seemed to have been over-zealous with the scissors but Basher was proud of the astonished crew-cut which bristled in the morning sunlight.

The girls wore their prettiest dresses and most wore nylons and high-heeled shoes. Mavis kissed her mother good-bye at the bus stop, then she settled down in the coach to apply a top-coat of lipstick. Mavis wore a blue sheath dress and was proud that she looked older than her years. She attempted a little harmless flirtation with the driver of the coach.

'You've got a handful here, Miss,' he laughed. He himself was a father of three and said that, in his opinion, people who were teachers either wanted 'their heads seen to' or 'deserved a medal.'

The Tots whiled away the journey by eating. They munched through sandwiches, pork pies, radishes, cream cakes, plums and chocolate. When we reached London the contents of forty brown paper bags were inside the Tots. I too had taken on ballast. I had an idea that I was going to need sustaining.

I had no fear that the Tots would be guilty of bad behaviour in public. I had given them a talk about upholding the honour of the school. They gulped down school-magazine ethics so I was fairly sure that they would be docile. It was that thought which made me uneasy.

They filed into their seats in the theatre and sat bolt upright and silent, like a row of well-trained zombies. Behind and in front of us uniformed Grammar school children were eating ice-creams, throwing the cartons at one another and behaving in the way the Tots usually behaved.

But the Tots, who were now well into their 'Fifth Form at St Swithun's' act, looked at the Grammar school children scornfully, mentally taking their names and numbers to report them to some 'jolly decent' Housemaster.

The other teachers looked curiously at the row of silent Tots. One woman said it must be interesting work to teach the deaf and dumb. That was before Titch spoke.

'Miss,' he said. 'Shall I collect the ice-cream papers and litter?'

'Yes.' I spoke quietly but the teacher in front of me turned, took us in (Junky's baseball cap included) at a glance, then threw us right out again.

Titch collected litter and Junky took the good-will mission even further. He offered his play programme to a Grammar school boy.

'I won't need it,' said Junky. 'I knows all about this play. There's these two chaps, see, and these two girls and they chases about in a wood. They gets mixed up cos' it's dark. Still, I spect they'll be able to see better in the daylight.'

The Tots took their first professional dose of Shakespeare in a silence broken only by a few astonished 'W-a-a-ah's,' 'W-e-e-e's' and 'C-a-a-aw's,' sounds which usually accompanied their getting to grips with a new idea. Afterwards they said that they had enjoyed the play, although some of the reasons given were not what I had hoped for.

'Caw, Miss,' enthused Junky, 'wasn't she a smasher, that girl who was Helena? Pity she had to wear them old-fashioned dresses. She got smashin' legs.'

Mavis and Dinny were sold on the good looks of the actor who played Lysander. They wanted to get his autograph, but the rest of the Tots refused to wait. They were heading for tea. On the subject of the opposite sex the Tots' reactions ranged from scorn to idolatry. The appeal of food was unanimous.

Steering a crowd of children through London on a steamy summer afternoon was difficult. I had to scurry through the ranks, periodically counting the Tots to make sure no one had been lost. The procession halted several times to collect stragglers. I worried lest I should lose someone and the Tots worried lest they should lose their tea. It was Basher who solved the problem.

'Count 'em once, Miss,' he said. 'Make sure they're all here then you march at the head of the line. I'll be at the back to see if anyone mucks about. If they do, I'll deal with 'em.'

So, with Basher's wrath at the stern and the prospect of tea before us, we arrived in good time.

It's difficult to barge into a restaurant with forty children in tow without being noticed. Diners stopped with their forks in mid-air. Two by two the Tots filed in. People looked around for a responsible adult and saw only a long woman in a limp linen suit. Some smiled pityingly. I didn't want pity. I was proud of the Tots. They would be back to normal tomorrow, but at the moment, they were giving a terrific performance.

They seated themselves four at a table. Now they felt grown up and on their own. At each table sat a girl Tot who had volunteered to pour tea and steer the less experienced through the formalities of ordering and paying the bill.

I sat at a table with Titch and Basher, who didn't care for being 'bossed about' by girls but accepted me as a natural hazard. Sandra also was at our table. Until recently she had been away from school with a throat infection. Her mother had allowed her to come on the outing only on condition that I kept an eye on her.

I wanted nothing more than refreshing tea, and Sandra wanted cream cakes. But Basher and Titch had been studying the menu and it wasn't purely academic interest. When the waitress came the boys put in an order which would have sustained fully-grown men for a day.

'My Mum don't like us to be finicky eaters,' said Basher, pushing a bunch of chips and sausages into his mouth. He looked disdainfully at Sandra's forking of her cream cake.

'And my Mum doesn't like me to be a piggy eater,' snapped Sandra, putting Basher neatly in his place. I was amazed that quiet Sandra had it in her. Basher too was nonplussed. After proving himself a responsible member of the Tots he didn't want to injure his reputation by cuffing anyone hampered by a cream cake. After the day of the outing I never again saw Basher use his fists to demonstrate his authority. It was no longer necessary.

The coach took us home through a countryside of cornfields reflecting the translucent light of summer. The Tots talked of what they had seen in London; people, sights, sounds. Someone even mentioned Shakespeare.

'It wouldn't be so bad if they didn't talk so old-fashioned,' Mavis remarked from the seat in front where she sat with Dinny.

'Still, I'm glad we went to see Shakespeare,' said Dinny.

'Yeah, so am I,' agreed Mavis.

Sitting contentedly in the warm engine-throbbing coach with the tired Tots around me I caught Mavis's words with sudden excitement. I had done it. Shakespeare had finally won through.

'Maybe now she'll give old Shakespeare a rest,' said Mavis.

'Who? Miss?' Dinny sunk her dark head against the back of her seat and nodded at the gathering dusk.

'Yeah. She do go on a bit sometimes, don't she?'

XV

On Open Day the school was host to parents and friends. Open behaviour came naturally to the Tots. They had open hearts, open minds, and more often than not, open mouths. Generously they flung wide both classroom doors, inviting visitors to come in.

The first thing to rush in was a gust of wind. It whipped through the room, scattering papers from desks and from the walls. The Tots re-captured and re-secured their exhibition work. Courteney prodded extra drawing pins into his traced map of Australia. It was a well-traced map and the spellings of the place-names were also well-traced. This, in Courteney's case, made it even more acceptable. A drawing of a kangaroo in a corner of the map gave Courteney a rough hint as to the correct way to hang Australia, always provided that he retained a nodding knowledge of the normal plumb of kangaroos.

Titch dusted off his sum book and replaced it on his desk. It was licked, from stem to stern, with red ticks and full marks. Basher replaced on the wall his drawings of British birds.

Dinny anxiously re-arranged two garments of indeterminate shape which she assured me were blouses which she and Mavis had made.

'You reckon it's time yet,' asked Dinny, 'for the parents to arrive?'

'Can't be time,' said Mavis, propping a fragment of mirror on the window ledge and arranging her blonde hair for the third time.

Mavis, like the other Tots, was of the opinion that the second the school gates were opened the crowds would immediately stampede to our classroom. Basher propped the doors open with stones 'borrowed' from Mr Avery's rockery, then he stood back.

Tensely we waited but no one came. The only sign of life was the school caretaker who dropped in to warn me that he would hold me personally responsible for the extra intake of dust particles incurred by leaving both doors open.

'Come and see our exhibits,' I said, trying to wheedle his tongue into a less abusive form of patter.

'Me?' Mr Hibberd's neck gnarled in astonishment. 'Don't I see enough of your old rubbish every day!' He bundled his mop more securely under his arm and shuffled across to the lavatories, bucket clanging.

I saw that the non-arrival of visitors, coupled with the remark about 'old rubbish' had undermined the Tots' self-confidence so I suggested that they went to the school gates to meet their parents.

I waited alone in the classroom, feeling nervous yet for no good reason. I knew most of the parents and looked forward to meeting them. But I suppose I was afraid of questions, the sort of questions which Mavis's Mum flung at me before she hardly had her feet over the threshhold.

'Our Mave been behaving herself, Miss?' Mavis's Mum was a well-defined blonde, her hair newly crisped and lacquered. Her flaring pink suit proclaimed that, like Mavis, she was an ebullient extrovert.

'Mavis works well when she wants to.' I was torn between loyalty to Mavis and honesty to her mother.

'But what, Miss?' said Mavis's Mum, turning over the needlework with obvious distaste. 'There's bound to be a "but" if I know our Mave.'

'Well,' I conceded, 'Mavis could do better if she talked less.'

'That's just what I always say.' Mavis's Mum dropped the blouse thankfully and snapped the air with a bright pink glove in a gesture of complete agreement. 'Mave's the same at home. Chatter, chatter, chatter all the time. Talk, talk, talk. Well, I say, I told her Dad, I don't know where she gets it from.'

She spent the next ten minutes telling me how she and her husband were the sort of people who hardly spoke a word. Finally she convinced me, at least about Mavis's Dad.

Several parents had now arrived and were looking round the 'exhibits.' Courteney introduced his father, a tall, lean man who wore a shapeless tweed hat. The turned-down brim shambled about his face. The face and the hat were the colour of old mustard. True, not much of the upper face was visible. Beneath the flap of the brim I caught only the flick of an alert grey eye.

Courteney always bragged that his father travelled a great deal. He would interrupt a lesson to look at his watch and announce, 'My father is just now taking off from Athens.' These remarks were greeted with gasps of awe from some Tots and jeers from Basher. Basher insistently maintained that Courteney's father had never risen higher off the ground than the top of a double-decker bus.

'I hope you don't hold with free discipline,' Courteney's father said to me suddenly. Mavis's Mum flicked a rhinestoned ear in our direction. She had developed a swift aural reaction to the word free ever since the welfare state and reading a book about free love.

'Children need taming, bringing into line,' said Courteney Senior. 'My schoolmaster used to make us sit bolt upright, backs against our chairs, arms folded. Six of the best for any boy who moved. Courteney give you any trouble?'

'No. His behaviour is good, but I wish his spelling would improve.'

'Spelling, eh? Isn't it time they introduced a phonetic system of spelling?' Courteney's father veered in my direction and as the hat brim lifted I caught a flash from a belligerent eye.

Basher took a listening brief in this conversation. Basher, I think, felt smug at finding Courteney's Dad with his feet planted so firmly on the ground. Also he too supported a swing to the phonetic in the way of spelling. Basher's spelling had long slouched in that direction.

Basher was now joined by an adult version of himself, his brother Lionel. Lionel was about twenty and had the same abrupt features and buoyant grin as his brother. He was an ex-pupil of Sunnyfield and seemed to know the staff on intimate terms.

'How's old Digger Avery then, Miss?' asked Lionel, sticking his thumbs into the slots of his leather jacket. 'Old Digger still stickin' the taters in upside down?'

Here was another embarrassing question. Like the one, 'Have you stopped beating your wife?' any answer was an indictment. I tried to steer the conversation into smoother waters.

'What do you think of Basher's drawings?' I asked.

'Not bad,' said Lionel, lifting a leather shoulder and taking a few paces backwards to squint at the drawings. 'Yeah,' he said, 'I suppose they could be worse.'

Basher was awash with such lavish praise from the lordly Lionel. His ears went a joyful scarlet. Lionel must have considered that he had overplayed the eulogy because he instantly back-pedalled.

'But he's a untidy little beggar, our Nipper, en ee?'

To my surprise Basher looked not crestfallen at this but more delighted. To round off his pleasure Lionel gave Basher a playful cuff. Basher looked as happy as a dog with two trees. The visitors in the room smiled at the brothers and a happy, relaxed atmosphere made people talk more freely.

A very free talker and free thinker was Junky's father, an affable man in a suit designed for a small coat hanger.

'What I say is,' Junky's father addressed a crowd of respectful parents, 'I say it's not what you know but who you know as counts.'

I felt that too much anti-educational propaganda already had been allowed to flow under the bridge that afternoon. I made a few dissenting noises but it was useless. Junky's Dad was now well into his spiel.

'My old Dad,' he boasted, 'he left school when he was eleven.'

Sweet William's jaw dropped in admiration and I felt that any day now he would be demanding his cards.

'And what's more,' said Junky Senior, 'do you know how my old Dad ended up?' The parents shook their heads and Sweet William crept closer.

'Bow-legged,' he bragged. Sweet William looked bewildered.

'Bow-legged with brass. Take it from one as knows,' went on Junky's Dad, 'learnin' don't get you nowhere.'

I felt educational security being bulldozed from beneath my feet, so I tried to whip up some interest in the exhibits. Sweet William's mother looked at a small wooden table which had been made by the boys.

'I made that leg, Mum,' Sweet William said, proudly indicating the only leg needing a wedge of cardboard beneath it. Sweet William's mother looked at the leg, her dark eyes full of admiration. She touched the wood reverently.

'You made it beautifully, son,' she said. 'What a pity they made the other three legs too long.'

Titch's mother's admiration for her son's work was equally ardent but less obvious. She paid little attention to the sum book. Titch, not a boy to be easily overlooked, thrust it into her hands.

'See, Mum? I got 'em all right.'

Titch's Mum allowed a twitch of satisfaction to flex her resolutely unimpressed mouth. Then she hitched her expression into order.

'So you ought to get your sums right,' she said tartly, 'what do you think we send you to school for?'

Titch grinned. He enjoyed his mother's offbeat form of approbation. He noticed that she carefully left the sum book on my desk, where it was less likely to be overlooked by other parents.

Junky's Dad, momentarily bored, was almost persuaded to look at the book. He was sidetracked, however, by the sight of a garble of small, bright red cubes beside my pens.

'Tippits,' said Junky Senior, clutching at the counters as at the hand of an old friend long thought dead. 'Well, I haven't had a game of Tippits since I was a lad.'

I suspected that his set of Tippits counters had gone the way of most. They had been confiscated by a teacher. Tippits was the local name for a game in which dice-like counters were tipped from the palm to the back of the hand. The skill lay in the number of counters caught and the acrobatic variety of sleights of hand as the game progressed.

'Used to be a dab hand at Tippits,' said Junky Senior. He flicked a counter and caught it on the back of his hand. Encouraged, he tried two counters and then more. Parents and children drifted from the educational exhibits to the sporting exhibits of Junky's Dad.

'That's not the correct way to throw Threesies,' said Courteney Senior. He took three dice and spun them expertly. His prowess brought a small gasp of satisfaction from the parents and Tots and a small grunt of derision from Junky's Dad.

'Three's easy,' he said, 'but six, now that's tricky if you like.'

'I could beat you, no doubt,' said Courteney's father. The challenge was accepted and the game between the two men commenced.

I tried to hustle a little more interest in the Tots' work and steer the parents' attention to the programme of music and drama which was soon commencing in the Hall. It was like trying to sell encyclopaedias to a Cup Tie crowd.

'I think we ought to have a Ladies' Match,' said Mavis's Mum. 'You got any more Tippits?'

I was about to say that I hadn't when Basher betrayed me.

'Miss got some in her desk,' he sneaked. I had temporarily confiscated Basher's set of counters when I had found him playing in class. For a week now he had been seeking a good excuse for their return.

I opened the desk and disclosed enough sets of Tippits to start a modest shop.

'Pink's my lucky colour,' said Mavis's Mum. She grabbed a puce set and she and Titch's Mum settled themselves in a desk to play.

'I'll have the yellow ones,' blurted Lionel.

'Green,' corrected Basher quickly, 'them green ones is mine.'

In a short while the classroom looked like a third-rate gambling joint. Money was not at stake but parental prestige was. The spectators gathered round the desks where play was in progress. As one by one the competitors failed the more complicated tests of 'Tippits' they retired. Only Junky and Courteney Seniors were left. The crowd gathered round them and excitement tensed to flash point.

It was neatly doused by the chastening sight of the care-taker. He stood in the doorway looking like the Slough of Despond on a wet night. He was wearing a soul-wracked expression and a coke-wracked boiler suit.

'What you doin' in this classroom? I suppose you know all the rest of them is watching the show in the 'all?'

Mr Hibberd looked suspiciously at the groups in the desks, at the coloured dice and the flushed faces. He was a man who had shunned all games of chance since he had once allowed himself to become over-fevered by a game of Snakes and Ladders.

'I dunno what you're up to in 'ere,' he warned me, 'but it's time for me to muck out this room. Four o'clock on a Friday I always mucks out.'

He took his broom and made a deliberate lunge at the cluster of spectators.

Junky's Dad was on the point of making a decisive throw of the game. The broom for a second joggled his attention. His hand faltered, the Tippits fell to the floor. He had lost the game to Courteney's Dad.

Under the onslaught of the rising dust storm parents and Tots dispersed to the entertainment and to tea on the lawn. Only Junky's irate Dad remained in the classroom, alone with the caretaker.

I don't know what words were bandied between the two men but when Junky Senior took his seat for tea he looked reasonably satisfied with himself.

'Like I said,' he announced, squelching into a cream bun, 'when it comes to puttin' folks in their place, learnin' don't get you nowhere.'

XVI

On the first day of End of Term Examinations ('Zams' in Tot-terminology), it rained reservoirs. Eapa's windscreen wipers flapped ineffectually, rain lashed in at the open window and I arrived at school damp but determined.

I was determined to act as the Tots' examination invigilator with patience and understanding. No child, if I could help it, would have the excuse for a bad paper of 'examination nerves.'

I was prepared to be co-operative but it seemed that the Tots had other ideas. Instead of forty Zam-eager Tots in the classroom I found only three. They weren't exactly avid for action. They were staring out disconsolately at the sheeting rain.

'Where is the rest of the class?'

'Dunno, Miss. School bus must be late. We come on our bikes.' They sighed, as if they were truly three of Life's Luckless.

The school bell rang and there was no sign of the bus. I began to worry. The three exiles also began to worry.

'We got to do the Zams on our own, Miss? Just three of us?' The Tots always preferred their ordeals thickly gregarious.

Suddenly there was the sound of running feet and Titch burst into the classroom. His head was as wet and sleek as an otter's and his raincoat was dripping.

'School bus broke down a-top of the hill, Miss,' he gasped. 'They sent for another bus but seein we was close to school we run for it as it was Zams today.'

Another crowd of wet and breathless Tots arrived and before many minutes had passed there was a full complement aboard. That they should race through a downpour in order to take 'Zams' was, I thought, a heroic act deserving full recognition. I sent a message to the Headmaster to explain what had happened. He sailed down to congratulate the class.

'I'll ask the caretaker to turn on the radiator in here,' the Headmaster said. 'It's not a warm day and the children will need somewhere to dry their clothes.'

The Tots settled down to their examination papers. Silence fell as they inscribed their names and form at the tops of their papers. I gave the usual spiel about no talking and going to the lavatory only if it was imperative. The question papers were handed out and the examination began.

The day had had a bad start but the Tots were calm and unruffled. As yet I saw no signs of examination nerves. Sweet William seemed particularly at ease. He sat nonchalantly undressing and was down to his braces.

'Is that really necessary, Sweet William?'

'I'm getting hot sitting by this radiator, Miss.'

'Oh, I see. Very well. Make yourself comfortable.' The Tots had endured a lot of water and inconvenience and I wanted to be reasonable and make them feel confident and reassured. If Sweet William felt more confident and reassured in his braces, who was I to carp?

My whispered words about 'make yourself comfortable' might as well have been shouted down a loud hailer. Every Tot seemed to have heard. (They always paid more attention to remarks which were not addressed to them.)

They started peeling off their coats, jumpers and cardigans and strewing them around the room; on the backs of chairs, radiators and on the floor. Raincoats hung from the window catches and the cupboard doors. Shoes were ranged along the window ledges. The classroom looked like the end of a busy Bargain Day at the Summer Sales.

It was not the well-organised examination day which I had visualised. But, I reasoned, it was the Tots who were suffering the real inconvenience. It was up to me to do all I could to help them. When I noticed Titch taking off his socks I tried to keep my voice controlled.

'Titch, you know there is a limit to making yourself comfortable. You must keep your socks on.'

'I got my feet wet running from the bus.'

To illustrate his point Titch held up his green socks and wrung water from them. I agreed that he could not work in soggy socks. Since other garments were cooking on all available radiator space I looked around for somewhere for him to dry his socks. Titch himself solved the problem. He pegged his socks to the cord of the window blind with paper clips, then hoisted them aloft.

At this, another nine Tots decided that their socks were wet and soon the windows were dressed overall with dank gaudy socks.

'I'm sure you didn't all get your feet wet.' It was my first word of reproof. I could just tolerate the room looking like a Bargain Basement but I drew the line at a Steam Laundry.

'Oh, yes, Miss,' said the Tots.

I suspected that the Tots knew they were gaining the upper hand. When I saw Dinny helping herself to a handful of new blotting paper I said nothing, although I knew that she already had the largest collection outside H.M. Stationery Office.

The examination was now well under way. I do not mean to say that the Tots were answering the questions but they were giving them their undivided attention. Sweet William stared at the maths question paper with an expression of deep admiration for the perplexity of the questions and shallow hope of the answers. Only Titch, the Arithmetical Wonder, worked ceaselessly as a small computer.

The laundry steamed away merrily, the nibs scratched and outside the windows the rain fell incessantly. Mr Hibberd, the caretaker, passed and gave a startled and accusing glance at the socks. I knew there would be a Note of Protest delivered that night through the usual diplomatic channels.

However, I had other things to think about. I noticed that Sandra was not writing and saw a tear trickle down her cheek. I tip-toed over to her and whispered.

'Don't worry about the hard sums, Sandra. Do those which you find easiest, then come back to the harder ones.'

'It's not the sums, Miss,' said Sandra. 'I feel sick. Mummy said I should make a good breakfast as it was exams so I had bacon and eggs.' Sandra said she did not feel that she wanted to be sick but her stomach was uncomfortable.

'Try one of my peppermints,' I suggested. 'They taste good and they may help you to feel better.'

Sandra took a peppermint. I crept back to my desk, hoping that our whispered conversation had not disturbed the class. It had, but not in the way I had imagined.

'Please, Miss,' said Linda, a sandy-haired scrap of a Tot, 'can I have a peppermint? I don't feel well. I think I've got a nervous stomach.'

'So have I, Miss,' claimed Jean. She and Sandra did everything together. I gave them peppermints and Mavis and Dinny decided that they also had nervous stomachs.

'So have I,' asserted Basher, who was as unlikely a candidate for a nervous stomach as you could find. Several Tots then laid claim to the affliction and it was only the eventual emptying of my peppermint packet which effectively halted the epidemic.

I doubt if any of the Tots except Sandra really felt ill but I could not afford to take chances. The class sat happily wriggling bare toes and crunching peppermints.

The rain coursed down the windows, obliterating the view of the Games Field, the pigsty and the dripping trees. As the examination drew to a close there was a cloud-burst of monsoon-like proportions.

'Look, Miss,' said Titch, pointing. 'There's water coming in under both doors.'

It was true. Water seeped in, trickled over the floor, spread into small lakes and finally into one large lake. The 'break' bell sounded but too late. We were marooned.

The situation was temporary but desperate. The Tots

sat on the lids of their desks and watched the water rise to the lowest rung of their chairs.

'I got me Wellies on,' said Junky, 'I'll go for help.'

It was hard to dissuade the Tots from paddling after Junky in bare feet but, having just dried them out, I was not keen on that idea. Junky returned with the caretaker, who seemed to think that the flood was my responsibility.

'It never happened before. Never,' said Mr Hibberd, leaning in at the window to contemplate our predicament.

'Can't you bale us out?' I asked.

'I daresay. When I got a minute. I got to see to me coke. The water got in me coke.'

I argued that our rescue should have priority over that of the coke. The caretaker did not agree.

'Water won't rise any higher,' he said. 'Will probably go down in an hour or so.'

'We can't wait an hour,' I said. 'The children have to get their milk.'

'And we got to go to the lavatory,' said Titch, always a stickler for accuracy.

Help was, however, at hand. Pinks Thomson and Mr Gideon appeared in boots and oilskins and looking like deep sea trawlermen about to face a rough night.

'Put on your shoes,' Pinks instructed the class. 'Then Mr Gideon and I will carry you out on our backs.'

The Tots whooped at this prospect of transport a little out of the ordinary. Mr Hibberd sniffed and went back to his coke. All our crew were 'saved' and even 'Miss' was evacuated without the use of a crane.

'Take your class into the Hall for the next examination,'

said Mr Norris. 'It's the only room we have free until your classroom can be dried out.'

The class found chairs in the Hall but no desks. They made temporary desks of window-ledges, the edge of the stage and the P.T. equipment.

The examination was an English essay paper so I told the Tots that, knowing the circumstances, I would this time excuse any lawless leanings in their handwriting. The Tots were pleased with this 'unrepeatable offer' from 'Miss' and did their best to give her something worthwhile excusing.

The essays were often flanked by marginal notes such as, 'This is where there was a crack in the boards of the stage,' or, 'I am writing this on the horse and the legs is too short.' There was also Sweet William's poignant addendum, 'I could have wrote better but I lost me good nib in The Flood.'

By the afternoon we were able to use our own classroom, although the floor was still muddy. If we moved our feet smartly we spattered the walls with mud. The Tots spattered each other and flicked a little on my nylons to show there was no class discrimination.

The class said it had had enough junketing around that day. The Tots wanted to do the afternoon examination in their own room. The papers had been given out when the caretaker appeared, bucket and mop in hand.

'Come to dry you out,' he said.

I said we were busy and could he come back some other time.

'No,' he said, 'I've got other things to see to. Besides, you can't let these children sit here in the mud!'

This seemed a remark out of character for someone who

not long since had been prepared to allow them to sit up to their ankles in water. However, I decided not to obstruct Mr Hibberd. The Tots needed the immediate benefit of a dry floor. And I needed the future benefit of freedom from the caretaker's communications about banana skins in the waste-paper basket.

While the Tots worked at their examination paper the caretaker worked at the floor. It was a geography paper and the Tots were engrossed and silent. Mr Hibberd took their silence as a personal affront. He clanked his metal bucket and wheezed noisily down the handle of his mop. A spare outline map fluttered to the floor. He picked it up, dried it on his overalls, and peered at it closely.

'Map of Canada, isn't it? My son lives in Canada, and I say it's a jolly poor map.'

'They have to fill in the principal rivers and cities,' I whispered. I pushed him a spare question paper.

'That's easy.' He dumped his bucket and mop and sat himself in a desk. 'Let's see, Montreal is about there.' He made a dot on the map, sat back and looked very satisfied. Encouraged, he made another random dot and settled down to do the rest of the examination paper.

Since Mr Hibberd wrote more quietly than he did anything else, it seemed an excellent idea. Peace had at last come to our examination day. I looked at the rainbow which now swung in the bright sky. I thought that examination days were, after all, almost pleasant. All they required was a packet of peppermints and a determination to keep your knees above water.

133

XVII

Sunnyfield, never a buffer of sobriety, ran off the rails at the end of July. Then credulity held a short 'silly season.'

Examinations were over, Sports Day was past, no plays were in production and no operas being 'done.' The staff were marking examination papers and writing end-of-term reports. For the children there was little to anticipate but the summer holidays and they were a week away.

To the Tots each summer day was as a lifetime and a week too long to contemplate. They were bored. They sat reading the library books one thundery afternoon. I worked at a set of reports which the Headmaster wanted completed by four o'clock. The windows were open but the air was oppressive and no birds sang.

The Tots knew I was writing remarks about them on the report forms and the atmosphere was burdened with apprehension and restraint. I looked up and saw Titch staring intently at my writing. I had once heard him boast that he could read an upside-down newspaper. He laid his head on his desk and squinted along the side of his nose.

Basher prodded him for the outcome and Titch shrugged his shoulders. He hadn't been able to read a word. Basher sighed and the sigh was repeated around the class. The Tots were in need of an occupation. When this happened they sometimes turned their attention to the most surprising subjects.

'Please, Miss,' Mavis blurted out, 'is Mr Gideon engaged to Miss Girlan?'

I looked up, completely thrown off course. Mr Gideon, far from being engaged, was a man who wasn't in the 'phone book, sexually speaking. He spent his evenings preparing lessons and his holidays visiting his mother. As far as I knew, he had no girl friends. Miss Girlan, on the other hand, was soon to become engaged to a naval officer.

'Nonsense,' I told Mavis. Nevertheless, at the back of my mind possibility stirred. The Tots, though groping murkily in most areas of knowledge, had a high-powered arc-light on the precinct of Other People's Business.

'You musn't imagine things, Mavis.'

'I didn't imagine it, Miss. Mr Gideon told us that he is going to marry Miss Girlan.'

All the Tots nodded in solemn confirmation. I was impressed but not convinced. I asked around the staff-room.

'No smoke without fire,' said Pinks Thomson, who as school fire officer kept an eye on all patches of likely combustibility.

'Well,' reasoned Miss Tonks, 'if your class say that they are engaged it must be true. Musn't it?'

Mr Critchley put the point less tactfully. 'Are your lot liars or aren't they?' I denied it vehemently, of course.

'We had better decide what we will buy them for a wedding present,' said Miss Slater. Her recent illness had opened her eyes to a good-looking doctor and to joys other than netball. She began talking of canteens of cutlery and clocks and asked me to go to town with her at the weekend to look round for a suitable wedding gift.

I said shouldn't we wait until we were sure of our facts.

'Now I come to think of it,' said Mr Avery, until now eclipsed by a seed catalogue, 'I did see Giddy and Girlie messing about at the back of the bicycle shed after school last night.'

Everyone in the staff-room stopped marking papers, wiping their spectacles and reading the book of the month.

'What were they doing?'

'Well,' said Mr Avery, trying to look like a man about to load the Sunday newspapers with a high-powered charge of lasciviousness, 'he was mending a puncture on her bicycle.'

The staff's interest went as flat as the tyre. I pointed out that the mending of a puncture hardly constituted even a minor skirmish on the outskirts of passion.

No one cared to question Mr Gideon or Miss Girlan. We liked to appear to be incurious while prying like ferrets.

The school became dense with rumours of the engagement and the staff said they didn't want to be the last to know. They decided that I must sink my pride and ask the Tots about their privileged information. I found an opportunity when I saw Mavis counting a pile of coins.

'You are rich,' I said.

'It's not my money, she said, 'it's what the class have collected for the wedding present.'

'Do you know when the wedding will be? I asked.

'Not exactly, Miss. Haven't you heard?'

'No. They seem to be keeping their engagement a secret

for the time being. But Mr Gideon told you, of course.'

'Well, sort of, Miss.'

'What do you mean, "sort of"?'

'Well, you see, Miss,' explained Mavis, 'there was this quiz in a magazine and it said what were the qualities needed for an ideal wife and Dinny asked Mr Gideon what he thought.'

'Yes?'

'Well, Dinny asked Mr Gideon if the girl he married would be a good cook and he said "yes".'

'Is that all?'

'So Dinny said would Miss Girlan make a good wife and Mr Gideon said that Miss Girlan was going to *be* an ideal wife, and very soon.'

I sighed.

'Mavis,' I said, 'I think you should hand that money back to the children. Mr Gideon said that Miss Girlan was going to be an ideal wife because we understand she is soon to be engaged to a naval officer.'

'Oh.' Mavis was for a moment perplexed, then she recovered.

'Never mind, Miss. We can keep the money and give the present to Miss Girlan when she gets married. You said she was going to marry a naval commander?'

'I did not. I only said . . .'

But Mavis was already on her way to break the news to the Tots. By now Miss Girlan was engaged to at least an admiral. That was how rumours grew at Sunnyfield. They sprouted like the 'carrits and unyons,' prodded and examined by the Tots.

I told the staff that the Tots had made a slight mistake. I said it was very easy for children of their age to misunderstand. The staff grunted and no one openly accused the Tots of being rumour-mongers, not in my hearing. I would have denied the allegation, at that time.

A few days later I arrived at school during the lunch-hour. I had been to visit the dentist. I found a group of Tots sitting in the classroom. They had gathered around Basher's desk where he was counting a pile of coppers. I thought the Tots seemed surprised to see me.

'Is that the money Mavis collected for Miss Girlan? You should give it back, I think, and make another collection nearer the time of the wedding.'

'This isn't the money for Miss Girlan's present,' Junky said. I thought he looked embarrassed. Junky scratched his head vigorously when perplexed.

I looked at the group. Titch was shifting from one plimsoll to the other, Basher's ears were flushed, Mavis said nothing and Sweet William tried to creep out of the room. The Tots looked guilty of something but I couldn't guess what.

'You weren't gambling for money?' Teaching had made my thoughts ignoble.

'Nah, Miss. Course not.' The Tots chorused repudiation.

'It's not gambling money, honest, Miss,' said Mavis. 'We collected the money for you.'

'For me?' I was both touched and bewildered. I could think of no reason why the Tots should subscribe for a gift for me.

'Yes, Miss,' Mavis went on, 'when you didn't come to school this morning . . .'

'I had to go to the dentist's,' I said.

'Yes, Miss. Well, nobody knew where you were and we thought you were ill.'

I looked around the covey of Tots, whom I now realised I had sadly wronged. I had accused them of gambling and, in my heart, thought they had as deft a hand with gossip as incendiaries with a match. Yet I had been absent for only half a day and they worried about me. I went into the cupboard and blew my nose noisily.

When the Tots had gone I walked among their desks, musing on my unworthiness. My hand touched a scribbled list of names which Basher had left on his desk. I began to crumple the paper in my hand. Two words at the heading of the list registered in my mind.

'Wreath List,' it said, or perhaps I imagined it.

I put the paper in the waste-paper basket and never thought of it again. Perhaps it was my fault. If you live cheek by jowl with rumour-raisers you ought not to commit an inflammatory act like going to the dentist.

XVIII

At the end of the Summer Term a school photograph was taken. Results proved it was a subject better left. Back-log photographs of the past hung on the Hall wall at Sunnyfield. Each was a black and white indictment of accumulative years, humanity and the photographer's palsied retouching.

Mr Cooch, the Photographer Extraordinary to the school, was a man who believed in serious photography. There was not a cheerful face on any of his photographs. In his youth he had been photographer to a military establishment. This had given him a taste for uniformity; rows and rows of peaked caps a regulation inch above the chin. About the human face Mr Cooch cared nothing. He would have preferred to photograph the whole school in armour, with visors in the regulation down position.

As things were, he compromised. He retouched every face to a regulation expression; thick black brackets of eyebrows and a thin horizontal nick for the mouth. On school photographs any mouths with upturned smiling tendencies were tweaked into the approved expression by Mr Cooch. And any undue liveliness of the eyes was rectified by inserting in their place pairs of dead black dots.

Thus the collective mood of the school looked, to say the least, unhinged.

Mr Cooch sold his photographs not because he made people look good but because he made other people look ghastly. There is a small sadist in everyone. Mr Cooch kept him supplied with relish.

When the Tots were told that they were to sit for the school photograph they were overjoyed. Most of them were not yet tall enough to have come face to face with the grim zombies in the Hall. Only Basher was high enough to brave the encounter. He returned with the report that on the photographs 'all the teachers looks real daft.' That, as far as the Tots were concerned, put Mr Cooch in the front row of modern heroes.

Like all great undertakings, the school photograph required fair conditions, a propitious wind and all available hands mustered. Mobilising the entire cast of Sunnyfield was difficult at any time. Presenting it in a corner of the playground at a time when there was not too much wind and not too little sun required an organisation something akin to that needed for launching the D-Day Armada.

'Hold yourself in readiness for Monday morning at noon,' the Headmaster instructed my platoon. 'You will be in the front line.'

'Wassat?' asked Sweet William, who was always suspicious lest he might be among the expendable.

He was reassured by Basher that the front line exposed him to nothing worse than camera shot and a standard of dress less garbled than usual.

'Wear your best clothes,' commanded Basher, 'all of yah.

An' Titch, less ave yah outta them pumps. People can see your feet good when you're sittin' in the front row.'

Basher impressed on the Tots that as they would be the only people on the photograph to be seen *in toto* it was up to them to present the sartorial façade for the whole school. Those in the rows behind might get away with Wellington boots and football drawers topped by a clean shirt. And those in the back row might even skip the clean shirt in favour of a quick hair-do with comb and water. But the Tots musn't present so much as a dilatory boot-lace.

On the morning the photograph was to be taken the Tots arrived at school wearing their best. They creaked down the steps of the bus in their new shoes and walked stiffly to avoid taking the edge off their creases. Some of the girls had basted the pleats in their gym slips and said they wouldn't remove the tacks until the last moment. The Tots also took a great interest in the appearance of the staff.

'Looka Pinks Thomson's new sports coat! En it smashin',' said Mavis. Pinks took a short cut through our room and seared our eyes with the most emphatic display of check seen outside a monster crossword. He said he had come to tell us about the new instructions for Fire Drill.

At Sunnyfield we prepared for a fire as efficiently as you can prepare for something which is unlikely and unwanted. However, to keep Pinks happy and the fire bell in tune, we occasionally stopped classes and presented ourselves in out of the way spots behind lavatories and the coke store and called the registers.

Most of the Tots, their eyes dazzled by the new coat, missed the best part of Pinks' instructions. When the Tots' eyes were working overtime their ears were less alert, and vice versa. If I wore a new dress I had to allow the class half an hour to absorb the novelty, ten minutes to enquire of each other 'what *do* she think she look like?' then we could settle to work. My outfit that morning had less than its usual time-allowance because there were so many other members of staff demanding the Tots' attention.

'Digger' Avery had abandoned his shapeless gardening gear in favour of a grey professional-type suit in which he looked, for the first time, as if he were about to conduct important negotiations in a commodity other than seed potatoes.

Mr Critchley flashed by in a blazer garnished by as much gold braid as a small scale naval manoeuvre. Miss Ritchie, a well-built breezy girl, usually wore a His and Hers sweater knitted in the His size. This morning she stunned us in a pink dress with pearls.

'Miss Ritchie looks very smart,' said Dinny, nodding her head approvingly.

'Yeah,' said Mavis, giving the blackboard a good clean before we went to Assembly, 'I dunno why teachers can't dress nice always.' She thudded the board-cleaner on my desk and left me coughing in a cloud of dust. Mavis encouraged no dress reform among teachers but overalls topped by plastic head-domes.

In Assembly, Mr Norris gave detailed instructions for the photograph; time, position, dress, inclination of head and facial expression. We were to look thoughtful but not downright depressed.

The morning passed slowly. Hedged by the restrictions

of their best clothes and the prospect of having their expressions controlled to the blink of an eyelash, the Tots felt fettered and morose. They cheered up only when the bell rang for us to go out to be photographed.

We were first out of the trap and found Mr Cooch waiting in the playground. The sun of early morning had disappeared. The sky was now overcast but Mr Cooch still wore a panama hat. It covered any meteorological doubts and a bald head.

The Tots thought they were to sit in the front row of chairs.

'No. No,' said Mr Cooch. 'The chairs are for the teachers. You must sit in front of them, on the ground.'

'Wa? Sit onna floor!' bridled Titch. Titch objected to being cut off at the knees when he had gone to the trouble of leaving his beloved plimsolls at home. The other Tots objected on the grounds of discomfort. The photographer had difficulty in persuading the Tots to sit. The Headmaster achieved the effect immediately. He appeared in mortar board and black gown flapping in the rising wind.

'Caw!' said the Tots, and sank to the floor, their knees buckled by incredulity.

'What *do* ee think ee look like?' Mavis gasped, but more in admiration than in doubt.

The other classes filed out and, line by line, took their places. The arrangements took a long time. The Tots' patience and the dwindling sun edged away. By the time all was ready the sky had blackened and rain seemed imminent. Only Mr Cooch seemed unaware of this. The sun,

I suppose, is an assumption natural to a man in a panama hat.

'Relax,' said Mr Cooch.

The Tots had been sitting for so long that they looked as rigid as a row of skittles. Mr Cooch wasn't satisfied. He ran backwards and forwards across the playground. He wanted to make sure that at least a part of everyone would be visible on the photograph.

He didn't mind how little was visible. It might be merely the top of a head or the end of a shoe-lace. 'The less seen the better,' seemed to be Mr Cooch's motto. An entire photograph tended to make people reluctant to buy. They said that they thought that they 'didn't take a good photograph.' What they meant was that Mr Cooch didn't.

So a portion might be tantalising enough to stimulate sales where the whole might be only harrowing. It made sense. By this method of fragmentary photography Mr Cooch reduced depression in the district to a more workable level.

By the time we were accurately stacked in tiers, rear rows wedged into the notches between the front row's shoulders, thunder grumbled.

'Fine. That's just fine,' came the muffled voice from beneath the panama. 'Relax and it will all be over in one minute.'

Actually it took less. A cold drench of rain swooped on the playground. In thirty seconds flat the scene was desolate. All that was left of our dash for shelter was a row of over-turned chairs and a panama hat.

Rain persisted so the photograph was postponed until the same time the following day. The Tots grumbled, re-basted their pleats and pressed their creases between drawing boards. The idea of appearing for a second day in their best did not appeal to them. They did so, but the edge had gone from their creases and their enthusiasm.

Titch had become so dispirited as to backslide into his plimsolls. Yet he still wore his best suit and his anachronistic tie decorated with Christmas trees. The other Tots, embittered by the frustrations of the previous day, had lapsed into sartorial deterioration below the knee and a martyred expression above the chin.

'Hope that Mr Cooch gets a shift on today,' sighed Toddy. He had denied himself, at Basher's insistence, the moral support of the pencil behind his ear and ruler down his sock.

'Rain again today I shouldn't wonder,' said Dinny, mournfully searching a cloudless sky.

'Nah,' said Basher. 'Weather man on the telly said it'd be fine. Nah, there won't be no trouble with taking the photograph today.'

I should have known that when the likes of Basher assume the role of Oracle, there's prophetic bankruptcy in Delphi.

But the sun did shine and things did go well. Because of our enforced rehearsal the previous day we fitted neatly and uncomplainingly into our appointed niches. We were ready for those annual few seconds when Sunnyfield, staff and pupils, made a human defencework, unassailable and rather thick.

The Headmaster occupied the central position. He was flanked by his staff in order of seniority and importance.

My position was on the far-flung outposts of the demarcation line between staff and pupils, the unwitting and the unwilling.

The photographer urged us not to sit like concrete plinths. He insisted that we behaved naturally. This the Headmaster took too literally. He made off at a gallop and we waited impatiently while he answered a telephone call and returned to his place.

'Now, at last, we are ready,' sighed Mr Cooch.

'Miss,' said Basher, 'Toddy wansa be sick.'

Toddy confirmed this and he and Titch made for the lavatories. No Tot was ever sick on his own. He always took someone to help him.

The waiting Tots, sitting on the warm ground at my feet, were ossified with boredom and cramp.

'How much longer Toddy gonna be?' Basher complained, 'I don't take this long to be sick.'

This provoked among the Tots a lively discussion as to the shortest time for the operation. I was glad when Toddy returned, looking very much brighter. He and Titch took their places.

'At last', The brim of Mr Cooch s panama sighed with satisfaction. 'At last we are all ready.'

He got us firmly in his sights. I remember thinking that, with our backs to the wall, we looked as if we were a large order for a small firing squad. The illusion suddenly lunged into life.

'Fire.'

The sound of the school fire bell stunned our ears. That bell did things to the school's reflexes. We had been trained to it for so long that our footwork now made a fair bid to the speed of light.

Reasoning, always a poor starter at Sunnyfield, was trampled underfoot. By the time good sense took command the fortress of humanity which Mr Cooch had patiently built and jollied along for the last two days had dispersed like smoke.

Only the members of staff who were more responsible and slow-moving remained on the photographer's canvas. Among these was Pinks Thomson. He made no claim to responsibility except the responsibility for the ill-timed sounding of the alarm. He had fixed a self-operating timing system on the alarm, set it and forgotten it. Fire drill now came as much a surprise to Pinks as to everyone else.

I had told Pinks that I admired his new system. It had the merits of spontaneousness and efficiency. It also had room for a deep black border of error.

The photograph was finally taken in haste and desperation. It now hangs at Sunnyfield, a permanent memorial to photographic defeatism. It is distinguished only by the panoramic flourish of the Tots. They sit, cross-legged and pert, out-facing all comers. Not even Mr Cooch has been able to curdle their expressions of flamboyant optimism.

It was the Tots' final triumph. They succeeded where all others had failed. They looked well, particularly well, when framed and glazed.